"Carol Gino, the other half of the Mario and Carol duo, has written a luminous portrait of the enchantment that happens when two people love deeply, work together on all levels and co-create wonders of living and invention."

—Jean Houston

ME AND MARIO

Also by Carol Gino

The Nurse's Story

Rusty's Story

Then an Angel Came

There's an Angel in my Computer

The Yardsale of Life: The 8 Coats of Meaning

Where Dreams Come True

The Family by Mario Puzo,
completed by Carol Gino

ME AND MARIO

*Love, Power & Writing
with Mario Puzo,
author of The Godfather*

Carol Gino

aaha!
BOOKS

Texas and New York

Printed in the United States of America
First Printing, 2018

ISBN 13-PB 978-1-936530-33-5
ISBN 13-Kindle 978-1-936530-40-3
ISBN 13 –ePUB 978-1-936530-35-9

Cover design: Aldren Gamalo
Cover design: Angelia Mansfield

Published by aaha! Books LLC
173 KLBJ RD
Smithville, TX 78957
www.carolgino.com
www.meandmario.com

aaha!
BOOKS

For Mario

Acknowledgments

I would like to thank everyone who has helped me in the writing of this book, especially my brilliant editor, Dusan Leon-Citic, who managed to convince me that less is more and helped me carve the angel from the stone.

To my Creative Director, Angelia Mansfield, who helps turn my words into visual art and keeps my website running and me grounded.

For Pinkie Bechtol and Janet Lee who read this story over and over all the years that we lived it.

I owe a debt of gratitude to both Judith Regan and Joni Evans who encouraged me to keep working on my story no matter what, and offered help when I needed it. To Mari who found the pictures and the typos. To Hillary Schupf, Shari Griswold, and Jessica Wani, who helped me get the word out.

I am more than grateful to Mario's family, my friends and my family—both here and in Serbia—for helping me and inspiring me to keep at it.

Of course, for Lynn, who is more than friend, more than family, and who manages my life always, but especially when I'm writing my books! And for my sister, Bibs, who always told me the truth!

To everyone else who has been a part of my journey, I thank you. I am grateful for the part you played.

Prologue

The Mario Puzo I got to know intimately over the 20 years we worked and played together—as lovers and best buddies—was much more than "the mafia man" his readers thought him to be. Yet, he did possess the same intelligence, cunning, and strategic thinking he gave Don Corleone in his book "The Godfather." He was as devoted to family, as reasonable, and as wary of betrayal.

In time, I found that Mario was even more unique and complex than any of the characters he created. And certainly funnier. He had a real understanding of people, and endless patience. In all the years we spent together, I don't remember hearing him say an unkind word about anyone.

In truth, he had several extraordinary gifts. He had true vision with the ability to see into the future and to distill the most complex ideas into simple concepts and language that anyone could understand. In the time we spent together, he taught me much more about life, love, power and writing than I had ever hoped to learn.

It's Pygmalion with a twist, a different kind of love story, that I feel I have to tell. Why? Because in today's world which lacks so much real magic, genuine passion, compassion, and true romance, Mario and I managed to sustain it. He was an authentic grownup who never forgot the value of his own heart, or the dreams he had as a child. And he helped me learn to value mine.

But don't misunderstand, there were still times we drove each other crazy and we did fight. Well, maybe that's not completely true, I fought with him, and he struggled to understand what I was trying to say. For in truth, we came from different species. He was, after all, a man, and I was, after all, a woman.

Mario taught me more than any other man that a relationship is not only about love, it is also about power. Power in all its disguises was something Mario truly understood. That was an aspect of human nature that fascinated him. His exploration of it was the basis of all his stories. He explained to me, more than once, that the kind of power he explored was the kind of power men admired. That was power in the "outside world."

He insisted that women were expert in a different kind of power. They knew more about inner power, and that was the kind of power he and I could study. It was the understanding of power in the outside world that he tried to foster in me. It was the inner power of women that he wanted to learn.

"Without a balance of power, there can't be equality in any relationship," he explained. "You want equality for women, right?"

"Actually, I want equality," I said. "I don't want women to get more money or more breaks than men. That throws the equality thing off again," I explained.

Mostly, I got it, and when I didn't, it was because he was, after all, a man, and I am, after all, a woman.

That we managed to love each other and understand each other in spite of that was in itself a miracle. That we were able to learn from and respect each other was an even greater miracle.

Mario often said he believed men would become extinct.

"No, no, they won't," I said, impassioned. "I can't believe that."

He smiled when he said, "Why? When women can do everything men can, then why will they need men?"

"For the differences they offer," I told him. "For their infuriating differences. They still make the world interesting. Besides, I'd rather compete with men, it makes the game more fun."

"How do you think men can be saved?" he asked me, and I could see he was sincere.

In a fervor, I told him, "Women have to stop treating men as men, and begin treating them as they treat other women. Then we can respect them. By manipulating them we just rob them of their chance. Then we lose our chance to see them for all they can be."

Mario laughed at me. "Whose side are you on anyway?" he asked.

"Ours," I said.

In remembering all those years we spent together, there was one defining moment which gave me hope that men and women could one day be equal and in the end, maybe even understand each other. As I look back on it now, it seems like such a simple thing....

It happened on one of those nights that I had gotten really whipped and worn down by life, had lost confidence in myself, in my dreams, in the benevolence of the world because I had been working too hard for too long, and I still had too many bills, and too many people I loved were in pain. I was losing my will to keep fighting. The final blow was that a patient I had taken care of had died, despite all our heroic efforts and a book I really believed in was turned down by my publisher. I was so heartbroken I couldn't even speak.

That night, all I could do was jump in my car, drive over to Mario's house, run upstairs and ask him to hold me. He didn't ask any questions. He just put his arms around me and lifted my chin when he said, "Don't worry about it, I'll never let you go down in defeat."

After all the wonderful places he had taken me, after all the expensive gifts he had bought me, after all the five star hotels we stayed in and all the exquisite restaurants we ate in, after all the celebrities we met and every other exciting thing we'd done together, my most priceless memory is that when I needed it most, Mario said, "I'll never let you go down in defeat."

It didn't matter that no one can do that for another, if life has something else in mind, what did matter was that on that night, he was not only Merlin, the magician, he was the Knight, he was the Godfather, he was the hero, and for once I could just stop being the "tough guy."

Instead, I could fold and be the damsel in distress knowing that he would save me from the fire-breathing dragon who was threatening to swallow me alive. Because on that day, I was a very tired feminist and it was such a comfort to know that Mario had my back.

ME AND MARIO

Chapter 1

When Mario and I met, I already had some Life under my belt—both good and bad. I was thirty-seven years old and I'd been married twice, once to a Prince and the second time to a Psychologist, and by then I had realized that sometimes a frog is just a frog.

I was disillusioned by the fairy tales and figured I'd never crack the code of "forever after" relationships. The closest I'd come was my 16 years as a nurse in the Hallowed Halls of hospitals where I could imagine myself a great warrior slaying dragons and stamping death and disease out of the Western Hemisphere. Healing was my true passion.

In the real world, I had two kids who brought me down to earth. So in reaction to my failed marriages, and in response to the 60's culture, I had spent much of my spare time marching in rain, sleet and storm for Justice and Feminism. By the time I met Mario, I had vowed to be independent and self-sufficient for the rest of my life and never to give myself up again for a man.

Mario Puzo was 58 years old then, had already written the story of "The Godfather"—the most romantic Patriarchy ever—and had just lost his wife, his greatest passion. For him, her death had been a mythic battle and because of it he had suffered the most terrible defeat of his life. He swore he would never again fall into the innocence of True Love. So we were joined together by common purpose: The Romantic Patriarch and the Radical Feminist. God's got a funny sense of humor.

That was the beginning of Once Upon A Time, in my fashion.

Destiny has a grand design, and sometimes looking back it becomes clear how each of us has been set up to fall into place...

The earliest remembrance I have of my childhood was when I was still a toddler. My father stood me up, held both my feet in his right hand and slowly lifted me higher and higher, warning, "Don't bend your knees. If you bend, you'll fall." Then he encouraged, "Keep your knees straight and you'll be fine." We practiced it time and time again until I got it right.

I swear I still remember how my legs felt, strong as steel, how I felt, even then proud of myself, though everyone says that can't be true because I was too young. The rest of my childhood was the continuation of my father's training of me as a Spartan youth. The other thing I remember from my very young life is that my father always talked to me. He shared ideas with me before I could even understand them. There was no night I went to sleep without my father reading to me, usually a Grimm's or Anderson's fairy tale, and we had no dinner without my father reading me arguments of the great philosophers from one of his leather bound books of the Harvard Classics.

As I got older my father continued to instill in me the love of learning, and the need for mastery. He challenged me often when I was young and as I got older I began to challenge him. He enjoyed the game, and the better I got at the competition of ideas, the more fun we had. He loved that I could hold my own in any argument. And he spent my childhood clapping for me.

The only downside of that relationship was that while both my father and I knew I was always competing to be a better me, the young men I went out with when I started dating thought I was challenging them. So they thought I didn't like them. Later, I'm afraid my husbands felt the same way, but I didn't get that either.

I didn't understand any of it until I was older, but by then I knew that in order to change it, I would have to be less than I could be. That came after I'd finish being angry with my father and all the other men I'd met who I believed wanted me to be less than I could be.

Actually, I had become even more authentically me after my time with Mario. Once I'd learned everything he could teach me about writing, and even more about love and power—after he was the one who helped me crack the code.

Chapter 2

We were sitting upstairs in Mario's study talking about writing, politics and power in relationships during one of our early conversations.

"There is no equality without economic equality," I told Mario but he disagreed.

"There may be no equality without economic independence," he said, "but there are many other kinds of power."

"Like what?" I asked.

"Men are attracted to beauty for one thing," he said. "Youth for another. That gives beautiful women a certain kind of power."

"That's more important to men than to women," I said. "Kindness, intelligence, generosity, and a sense of humor are more important to women."

Mario sat back and just looked at me. He seemed to be thinking. "For young love, innocence and passion are necessary virtues," he said smiling. "For real love its important to understand power and how it works. There, partners should be equals."

Mario also tried to set me straight about writing very early in our relationship. We were again sitting upstairs in his study in his house on Long Island. "I wouldn't want anyone I loved to be a writer," he told me. He was in his usual "thinking'" position, leaning back in his leather chair, smoking a huge dark Hoya de Monterrey cigar, his bare feet resting on his large wooden desk.

"Why?" I asked him. "I thought writing was your greatest passion—the most important thing in your life—the only thing you would ever fight for. You told me that at one time you were ready to relinquish everything else in your life—even your wife and family, no matter how much you loved them, because writing was the only thing you could take seriously, no matter how ridiculous that seemed to people who weren't writers."

He looked up as he studied me. "So, what's your point?" he asked amused.

"I don't get it," I said. "Why wouldn't you want someone you loved to share your passion?"

"Let me count the ways." Mario said and smiled.

"I want to learn to be a better writer, so I can help patients save their own lives. But I remember reading somewhere that you said writing can't be taught."

"Ahh!" he said. "But, if someone has talent, endurance and the courage to come clean, he or she can learn the *carpentry* of writing." His expression softened. "I don't usually give advice, but here I'm an expert so I'll take the chance. You have to believe me. Writing is too tough a life. You're already a terrific nurse and you love it. A person should only be a writer if he or she has no choice. Never to make money. It's too much of a long shot."

"But you made money on The Godfather," I reminded.

"That was after 30 years of writing. That was after I had written two books that were hailed as minor classics that earned me less than $5,000. I was poorer than ever. By then I was 48 years old, had five children and I felt like a *chooch* because I couldn't earn a living to support them. Over all those years I suffered countless humiliations, so finally I gave up and sold out. That's why I wrote 'The Godfather.'"

"Why was that book a sell out?" I asked.

"Because I thought of myself as a literary man," he said. "I was committed to the art of writing. I admired Tolstoy, Dickens, Thomas Mann and Dostoevsky."

"I loved Pearl Buck, and Madame Curie, and Saints and Leper stories," I said. "Oh, and Philosophy and Mythology."

"The Brother's Karamazov' changed my life," Mario said, "I was a young kid growing up in New York's Hell's Kitchen. Every day I watched the people in the neighborhood struggle in dead-end jobs just to put food on the table. I knew that kind of life would kill me. So in order to escape the desperation, I hid in books that I borrowed from the New York City Library. Those books took me to other places, they gave me hope that I could escape the dreariness of the life I saw around me every day."

"But when did you know for sure you were a writer?" I asked.

He lifted his arms and put them behind his head. "A teacher told me," he said, remembering. "That's why teachers are important. I still remember her name after all these years. Mrs. Tyler. I wrote an essay she said was good enough to be published. I was twelve at that time and that day I walked home whistling."

"What did your mother think?" I asked. "Did she know you wanted to be a writer?"

Mario shook his head and frowned. "No, I used to daydream all the time when I was a kid and I didn't talk a lot."

"She never read your papers?" I asked.

"She couldn't read," he said simply. "A lot of the immigrants who lived in Hell's Kitchen at that time were illiterate. Also, she thought I was a little crazy, she probably believed I still wanted to be a magician."

"Why did she think you wanted to be a magician?"

"I must have been about nine or ten when I first read about King Arthur," he explained. "I was fascinated by the magician, Merlin, and all I could think about was magic. So one day when I came home from school, I tried to fry some pennies into gold."

I laughed. "What happened?"

"Well when she came upstairs from sitting on the stoop with her friends, I was in the kitchen and our apartment was filled with smoke. She pulled the frying pan off the stove and hollered at me. 'What are you trying to do, kill us?'" Mario shook his head, remembering. "When I told her what I was doing, she didn't laugh. She whacked me on the side of the head and said, 'Next time use the good olive oil, and fry them longer.'"

"So even then you were a magician. You were already practicing alchemy."

"I never tried frying pennies again, but what my mother said that day helped me as a writer. It's all the same. Magician, writer."

"She was funny," I said. "And you're funny..."

"Now tell me about you," he said. "Did you always want to be a nurse?"

"No," I said. "When I was young, I wanted to be a saint or if I had to settle, I wanted to be a nun. But as I got older and realized how much I wanted justice and liked to argue, I figured being a lawyer was a better fit."

"A saint?" he said, with disbelief. "A nun? Never. A lawyer? Maybe. But it was better that you became a nurse. You're a terrific nurse."

"You sound like my fifth grade teacher, Sister Robertine, who told me that if I really did have a calling to be a nun, I should join a cloistered order like the Carmelites so no one would know. That was one of my biggest childhood heartbreaks."

Mario threw his head back and laughed. "Why does that strike me as so funny?" he asked, but before I could answer, he added, "How did you go from being a saint to being an ardent feminist and liberated woman?"

"My Italian father told me I could do anything I wanted to if I wanted it badly enough. So I had no understanding of society's restrictions for women and no knowledge of how little law had to do with Justice. Still, I also had an Italian mother who told me what was expected of women. I thought she was crazy, of course. I didn't pay enough attention to her. She managed to stay married for over 35 years."

Mario was silent, thinking. After several minutes, he pronounced, "Soon marriage is going to be extinct, you know. Women will figure out that it's an emotionally bankrupt institution because a wife is a possession and they no longer want to be owned. And if women are equals, what good are they to men? I mean why would a man who thinks of himself as a chivalrous knight want to save a woman who can take care of herself? Especially if that means she can do anything she wants?"

"Because they like each other and want to spend time with each other?" I suggested. "It doesn't have to be the kind of contract it always was. Besides, in that kind of a marriage there wouldn't be the kind of guilt you felt when your wife died, because you wouldn't have felt so responsible for her."

"A husband is a husband and a wife is a wife. As soon as you change the roles, it no longer works for either of them."

"I like marriage as an alternative lifestyle," I said. "The contract can be amended, and a new kind of marriage can evolve."

"So you still want to be married?" he asked me, astonished.

"I always wanted to be married for 50 years because I hate failing at anything. But it is possible that because I want to do whatever I want to do, I'm too hard to get along with."

Mario looked amused, "You don't have any idea how outrageous you are, do you?"

"Well, enough men have told me I'm different for me to have a clue," I said. "But I don't really get it. Do you really think I'm outrageous?"

He laughed, "Sure," he said. "But in a good way."

"The truth is that if I can do whatever I want to, I'm a truly happy person," I explained, "but otherwise I'm no fun to be around. I guess that in itself is kind of outrageous."

"No," he said thoughtfully, "There are a lot of people who get what they want and still aren't happy."

I just have to get it through my head that marriage is something that I can do, but not something I do well. No matter how hard I try. And no matter how much I love, I just can't be what a man wants me to be. I keep being me."

Mario took his feet off the desk and sat up straight. "You remind me of my mother and my sister," he said. "That's the good news..."

"What's the bad news?" I asked.

"You remind me of my mother and my sister." Mario threw his head back and laughed.

"Very funny," I said. "I mean really funny."

"I have to be careful," he told me. "Most people don't get my sense of humor."

Later, we talked about his kids, and mine, and later on that night, after we had dinner was the first time I heard him describe The Godfather as an Olympian family myth.

We were sitting in the living room in front of the TV and the movie "The Godfather" came on.

"What I don't get, and what you still never answered, is why you feel like you sold out by writing The Godfather.'"

"Because it's not literature, it's a commercial novel. I felt I wrote beneath my gifts to feed my family, not for love of art," he explained, "But the funny thing is that selling out eventually brought me to my true gift. That of a storyteller."

"See, you never would have come to that if you hadn't been desperate. So, now I'm asking you, can't we give it a shot and see if I can learn to write? Underneath the nurse in me, there could be a terrific writer. I'm smart, I love books and even more, I love mastery. Let's see if I can learn the carpentry of writing."

"Don't say I didn't warn you," he said, his eyes glittering with amusement.

Relaxed, I admitted, "You know, when I read that book, 'The Godfather,' I thought you were just another male chauvinist pig, and I didn't understand why everyone was making such a fuss over it," And then I told him, "I would never have gone out with you if you were like one of those guys. In fact, I probably would have killed you."

He reached for another cigar from the humidor on his coffee table and struck a match to light it. Without looking up, he said, "I like tall blondes."

"Okay, so you wouldn't have liked me either," I said. At 5' foot 2" with dark hair, I got it.

He looked up at me, expressionless, and said, "We would have killed each other."

"You hardly know me," I said to him. "How could you know that?"

Yet, I was afraid he was right. From the time I was a little kid, I swore I'd rather be imprisoned for life than marry an Italian man. I grew up in an Italian family watching my mother cater to my father while my father talked to me.

Mario shook his head when he told me, "The truth is that I was surprised that so many women liked the Godfather. I wrote it as a story about a man and his sons—as a family story—with all its loyalties and betrayals. But essentially it was a male myth."

"That's why I think it made me crazy, because the women were so thinly drawn, so wimpy that they were almost invisible," I said. "Where were the real women, the strong women, the courageous women?"

"That was a different book. That book is 'The Fortunate Pilgrim,'" he said. "Besides, women are already heroes, they don't need myths."

"Are you trying to con me?" I was wary now. He was cunning after all.

But he looked thoughtful and sincere. "I really believe the only war left to be fought for evolution is the war between men and women. That will be The Last Great War," he pronounced.

"I don't get it," I confessed.

Mario explained, "As long as men fight only with other men, they're fighting the same war over and over again just with different players. Women will change the rules and goals. They'll play for different stakes; use different strategies and that will make it a different game. Maybe then we'll get someplace."

"Picture that," I said. "You, the creator of the great romantic Patriarchy, and me the ardent 60's feminist who marched for women's rights and fought for equality in everything." Now, I teased him, "By the way, I'd be wary if I were you. Don't underestimate me. My father always told me that I came from a long line of pioneer women."

Mario looked at me, studied me, and didn't answer for a long time. But from *the look* in his eyes, I knew he was thinking. Finally, he spoke. "It does interest me, this war," he said, "And it will help pass the time."

Chapter 3

The first time I slept with Mario was at Joe Heller's New York City apartment. We weren't planning it, we had gone into the city to meet Mario's agent, Candida, so he could discuss a new writing project with her and he asked if I wanted to come along to get some idea of how the business worked. Afterwards, we planned to shop for books at Doubleday's on 5th avenue, and to walk around the city.

Time seemed to fly by. We had walked uptown 13 blocks, talking the whole time, and both of us were exhausted.

"My friend Joe's got an apartment around here," Mario told me. "Let's go up and rest for a little while. Then we can take our time looking around the bookstore."

"Sounds good," I said. "He won't mind?"

Mario just shook his head. "After the bookstore, we can get something to eat at one of the fancy restaurants here, or we could go up to Elaine's."

"If I have a choice, I'd like French," I said. "Is that okay?"

"Sure," he said. "Whatever you want."

I smiled and he put his arm around my shoulder. "So you like French food?" I asked.

"No," he said simply. "I like Italian or Chinese."

"But then why would you say yes instead of saying 'I'd rather go to an Italian restaurant?"

"The French have great cheese and I like cheese. They also have terrific baked goods, crusty breads and the richest desserts. Even more important, my dear, you said you wanted to go."

"That was easy," I said. Mario looked at me and laughed.

Joe's apartment building was in midtown and once we got there we had to take an elevator upstairs. "I hate elevators," I told Mario. "I hate apartment buildings. I worked in a burn unit long enough to always want a fast exit. Human beings are quite fragile, you know. Within a couple of minutes they can be turned into crispy critters."

"Charming, my dear," Mario said.

Once outside the apartment, Mario rang the bell. But there was no answer. Then he knocked. But still no one answered.

"Well, I guess this shoots visiting with your friend, Joe," I said.

Mario looked at me puzzled. "I wasn't planning to visit with him," he explained. "I just wanted to make sure we didn't disturb him." Then Mario bent down and picked up the key from under the welcome mat. He held it up to show it to me, and then opened the door to let us inside.

"Nice place," I said, looking around. It was plain but tasteful, all in pale blues and greens.

"Want something to drink?" Mario asked me as soon as we reached the living room. "No thanks," I said. "I don't drink. It gives me a headache."

I still don't remember how we got into the bedroom; I don't remember what I was thinking. I am sure I was still talking when Mario first kissed me. Before I knew it there we were, making love, and my life had taken another left hand turn.

I was trying to think about what I wanted to say when the phone rang and startled me. "What are we going to do?" I asked Mario.

"Let the answering machine pick up," he said, and just smiled a reassurance.

"Hope you kids are having a good time," the answering machine played.

"Oh my God," I said.

Mario shook his head. "That's Joe's idea of a practical joke," he said.

"He knew you were bringing me here?" I asked horrified.

Mario quickly protested, "He doesn't know it's you. He doesn't even know you. I just told him I might be stopping by with a friend."

Now I frowned. "This is all too well planned to be spontaneous."

"That's not true," Mario said. "A guy can always hope to get lucky, but that doesn't mean he will. So thank you," he said, and kissed me on the nose.

Suddenly it hit me! I sat up in bed, pulled the sheet over my head, and started to cry.

Mario was lying next to me completely relaxed, his arms folded under his head. "Was it that bad?" he asked, turning his head to look at me. Then he reached over to the night table for a tissue and handed it to me under the sheet.

"No," I said, sniffling, and dropping the sheet so I could see him. "It's just that now my whole life is going to fall apart."

"Why?" he asked, with a slight smile, "Was it that good?"

"No," I said as I blew my nose, "But it was good enough that once I decided to go through with it, I have to leave my husband. So in this one moment, with this one action, my marriage is over, my children will be crushed, I'll have to work twice as many shifts and I've just set everything else in motion that goes along with being a single mom again."

Mario looked sympathetic when he asked, "Do you want a soda?"

"No," I said. "But I do want a quick solution."

Mario got himself a soda and came back to sit on the bed. "I thought you were separated from your husband," he said. "You don't have to tell him."

"I would never cheat on anyone I was married to. But now that I've slept with you, I know I'm done. As for the 'separated' part, I am."

"Does your husband know?" Mario's asked, his eyes studying me.

"Well, six months ago I told him I wasn't happy," I explained. "But he said it wasn't his job to make me happy."

"It isn't?" Mario said. "I always thought it was my job to make my wife happy. Even though I didn't always do it." He laid back down on the bed again and said, "I remember the first time I knew we didn't see our marriage the same way. We were at a party and someone asked how we liked being married. I answered 'We're really happy.' But my wife set me straight by saying, 'You're really happy.'" He shook his head in disbelief as he remembered. "I was completely stunned. It had never occurred to me that she wasn't as happy as I was."

"Didn't you ever ask her if she was happy?" I said. "Because I did say months ago that if I wasn't any happier in six months, I was leaving. I've seen too much death and disease in nursing to give my life away. I don't want to live an empty passionless life."

"What did he say when you told him that?" Mario asked.

"He told me to do what I had to do," I said. "But I don't think he meant this. I don't even think he believed I would ever leave because his first wife threatened to leave him for thirty years but eventually he left her."

"He left a woman who was his wife for thirty years?" Mario said, surprised. "The mother of his children? Why?"

"Boredom, I think. He didn't want her to like being a housewife any longer. He wanted her to go to school and be more independent, but she didn't want to," I said. "There are a lot of details I never asked. I just took a trip to see a friend of mine in Berlin that year and when I left Ned was married, when I came back he wasn't."

"How did she take it?" he asked me.

"His wife you mean?"

"Yes," he said. "Was she okay?"

I shrugged. "Maybe she was as ready as he was because within the year, she was married to an Italian guy who just loved that all she wanted to do was cook and serve him."

"Do you still love him?" Mario asked.

I made a face at him. "Of course I love him or I wouldn't be living with him, but now that I've slept with you, I've apparently made the decision to leave him."

"Don't leave him for me," he said. "I don't want that."

"I'm not leaving him for you," I told him. "I'm leaving him for me. I'm leaving him because I was able to be with you, and feel closer to you than to the man I've lived with for seven years. That's a clue it's time to leave."

"Don't be hasty," he said deadpan.

Involuntarily, I laughed. "Don't worry about it," I said. "You're not involved really."

"I don't know whether that's a good thing or a bad thing," he said. "But before you leave your marriage, you should give it some thought."

I frowned and made a face. "I have thought about it or I wouldn't be here. I'm pretty pragmatic, when the pain outweighs the pleasure, I leave."

Later in the living room with both of us sitting on the couch, Mario said, "You know we can never have a great love affair."

"Okay," I said. "But why would that be?"

"Because each of us is too headstrong, and too selfish to love anyone else more than ourselves," he said.

"I'm not sure that's true," I told him. "I've spent my whole life taking care of and doing service for other people."

"Yes, but while you're doing all that good for others, you still do what you want to do for yourself. So do I," he explained.

"I thought that was healthy," I said.

"It may be," he said, "but it's not the kind of virtue you need to have a great love affair."

"Passion is what it takes to have a great love affair," I told him laughing. "Not virtue."

Mario smiled and asked, "Well, did you feel great passion for me or did you sleep with me because you felt bad for me because my wife died?"

I hesitated. "Well, it's not that clear. I did promise your wife I'd keep an eye on her family. You included. That's what she was worried about."

"This is your idea of keeping an eye on me?" Mario said, laughing again. "I'm sure she would appreciate it."

I smacked him playfully. Actually it was my truth, no matter how warped it sounded...

Several months before, I had been a private duty nurse taking care of Mario's wife, Erika, while she was dying of cancer and I had grown very fond of her and her family. Mario and their five kids had kept her at home, doing all the physical care themselves, and I spent the nights teaching and helping so whenever they could take a break, they could get some rest.

If she hadn't woken up sweating and shaking that one night that I was taking care of her, if I hadn't known she was dying, my life would have been completely different. But in that one moment, in that very moment she said, "How can I leave him and my children? How can I leave knowing there's no one to take care of them?" I made her a promise that completely changed the trajectory of my life. Erika had great courage and grace when she told me about her real concern for her family. It was on that night that I made her a solemn promise, "I'll keep an eye on them and make sure they're all right."

Somehow that became a vow for the nurse in me, something that held me accountable to a higher order. It was that oath as a healer that I honored above all else during that time.

The following week after the promise, I was reading a medical journal that stated, according to new research, the average number of social security checks the remaining spouse in a long-term relationship collected was eleven. The partner who was left lived less than a year.

Mario and Erika had been married for over thirty years. In my mind, that meant he was done for. His life would be over in eleven months if the research was right. I felt obligated as a healer to do something about it.

According to my interpretation of Freud, the only thing that could battle Death was Love. Eros or Thanatos. I had no choice. To save Mario's life, he had to fall in love again. Magical thinking, maybe even hubris, but at the time, that was my truth.

In fact a few nights before I had made the promise to Erika, I had a dream that I was walking along the shore around a lake with my husband, Ned, and we were admiring the tall green trees and flowers of a beautiful park, when suddenly I saw Mario flailing in the middle of the lake. His arms were waving. He was drowning. Without thinking, I jumped in to save him. Which in itself is funny because I can't swim. Besides, later I found out that Mario wouldn't be caught dead in a lake. But that was how I found myself in Joe Heller's apartment—To save Mario's life. For Erika.

Now, back in Joe Heller's apartment, I said to Mario, "Let's go out and get something to eat and go to the bookstore. I need to buy some books. That always makes me feel better."

That seemed to cheer him right up. "I'll buy you all the books you want," he said. Then almost as an afterthought, he asked, "Are you going to tell your husband what you did?"

"I don't lie," I told him.

"Why not?" Mario asked.

"I think it's demeaning. I'm an adult and if I didn't believe in what I was doing, I wouldn't do it," I explained. "I can't allow anyone to compromise me like that. I'm not a child. Besides, to be fair, I've made a choice and I have to allow him to make a choice. He can't really do that without all the information."

"Maybe he doesn't want to know," Mario said. "Maybe he likes the illusion of a happy marriage."

I looked over at him. "Maybe you're right," I said. "But I can't allow him that. It offends my sense of justice. If I break a vow, I have to allow him an out. Though I must admit, when we were married, I did have faithful, obey, and until death do us part stricken from our marriage vows."

"What's left?" Mario asked.

"Love," I said. "Respect, honor..."

Mario just nodded. "Well, whatever you do, if we wind up seeing each other, don't ever tell me the truth if you betray me. Deny it at all costs," he said, and I could see he was serious.

"Why would you want me to do that?" I asked.

"I believe in true love," he said. "I don't want reality. Besides it will put me in a terrible position because once you admit a betrayal, you force me to action. If you deny it, I can keep my illusions and I don't have to do anything at all."

"That's a nutty way to think," I said. "Interesting, but nutty. How could you ever trust me and why would I want to live with that kind of a lie?"

"Don't be a coward, Carol," he said tousling my hair. "Guilt is the price you have to pay for your sins. Remember, if you ever betray me, never confess."

Chapter 4

Mario dropped me off at home later that night with a mountain of books in my arms. By then both of us had decided that we should try being friends for a while and give up the sleeping together. He was still too raw from Erika's dying, and not thrilled about going out with someone who was still married. I agreed because I wasn't willing to lie to Ned.

During the following week, I tried several times to tell Ned about that day in the city. I actually went into his office on the other side of our house the very next evening to try to talk about our marriage, about how we could make it better, and about Mario, but Ned said he was too beat to handle anything heavy. Then he confessed, "The whole time we've been married, I've missed talking about trivial things. You know, just light conversation over breakfast or dinner."

I shook my head. "Wrong girl," I said.

Intimacy for me was dueling with ideas, fighting over politics, arguing for something each of us believed in. Exploring consciousness and the human condition was one of my favorite things to do. Ned couldn't have cared less about any of that. He said it felt too much like work. He was a psychologist who listened to people's troubles all day long, and he didn't want to come home and have to listen to mine.

Just before I left Ned's office that night, he hugged me affectionately and told me with a mixture of wonder and disappointment in his voice, "This relationship has always felt more like an affair than a marriage to me."

"Really?" I said. "Because honestly, to me this has always felt like a marriage, even when we were having an affair."

Later, I called Mario to talk to him. I explained that I knew I should leave Ned because no matter how each of us tried, we weren't what each other needed. We were making each other miserable. Mario encouraged me to give it another try and told me to be patient.

He reassured me that we could still be friends, I could come over his house and we could always talk about reading, writing and ideas. He enjoyed talking to me, and he believed I really should write a book about how important nurses were to the families of dying patients, even more important than doctors. Not only short stories. Then he offered his suggestions in discussing and developing the writing of that book.

"I'd be happy to help you," he said. "After all, we are combat buddies and you saved my life on that first night with Erika. You were a great general."

Over the next few weeks, I tried to do what Mario suggested, and examined all aspects of my marriage. Once I considered how it would affect all those I loved, I decided to give it one last gung ho try. I mean a full out, no holds barred, real hearted try. As long as Ned wouldn't try to stop me from being friends with Mario so I had someone to talk to, I'd try my damnedest to make it work.

It was three weeks later that I called Mario to find out how he was doing and he asked if I wanted to come over for a chat the following afternoon. He asked me how my book was coming along, and said we could toss around some ideas.

That night Ned would be seeing patients until late, so I agreed. Both my kids were teenagers and after school I knew they'd be hanging out with their friends. Even my English friend, Frany, who lived with us, helped me watch my kids, and take care of the house, would be working late at her floral design shop.

"Okay," I said to Mario, "We're on. See you tomorrow."

"Bring some of your work," he reminded. "I want to see what you've done."

When trying to describe my life to anyone who asks, I always tell them that I follow the iridescent arrows of Fate and watch how my life unfolds. Mario was a perfect example of that. Before I met him, I had taken a couple of writing courses at New School for Social Research in New York City and had completed a writer's workshop at Hofstra University on Long Island. That was all. At the time, I was bent on stamping Death and Disease out of the Western Hemisphere and was getting too tired to fight for my patients one at a time. The only solution I could come up with was to let the public know what was going on in the hallowed halls of Medicine. I wanted them to be better informed so they could at least protect themselves from harm. The Health Care System, as it was, needed to be changed. I had finally realized, I couldn't do it alone.

Writing was the one way I could arm my patients with information when they came into hospitals where the nurses and doctors would only speak in jargon the patients couldn't understand. The whole medical profession acted as though they were sworn to secrecy. The only way for them to keep their power was to keep the secrets. A lot like Mario's mafia, without the loyalty

"You don't have to go over my writing," I told Mario. "I don't want to take advantage of you."

"I want to see it," he said. "It's not for you, it's for me."

"Thanks," I said. "I'll be there about 1 pm. Will that work for you?"

"It's the perfect time," he said. "I'm looking forward to it."

"Great!" I said. I always felt better after I spoke to him and I was looking forward to spending some time with him. He had this great gift of being able to really listen so I felt I was being heard, and he was so smart we could intellectually fence which always had us both laughing out loud at the odd way each of us thought.

That morning I got out of bed early, and as I made my tea, I realized that for the first time in a long time, I was humming. Frany was sitting across the breakfast table from me and asked, "Is there something happening that I should worry about?"

"Nothing at all," I said. "I'm just happy."

Still, Frany looked worried.

That afternoon just before I left for Mario's, I grabbed a bunch of the short stories I had written for the Hofstra's writer's conference and several poems and threw them into an envelope to bring with me. I also brought the beginning chapter of the "book" I wanted to write.

It was a beautiful day outside, crisp and cold, but clear. The clouds floated in the pastel blue sky and birds flew overhead making it seem more like spring than winter.

In my car, I turned the volume up on radio and sang along as I drove the 15 minutes from my house to Mario's. I was a little nervous about what he would think about my writing but it was an opportunity to learn, and I've always loved learning.

His daughter Virginia, a sweet and pretty young girl, and her friend, Barbara, let me into the house.

"Dad's upstairs in his study," Virginia said, smiling. "Just go up."

I scaled the steps. Mario was sitting at his desk wearing a white Fila sweat suit. He was leaning back in his leather chair with his feet up on the desk. Barefoot as usual. As soon as he saw me, he stood up and smiled.

"Want a soda?" he asked.

"I'm okay," I told him. "I'll get it if I want one."

"Good," he said, as he sat again. "Make yourself comfortable."

I sat in a chair opposite his desk. Almost immediately, he reached for the envelope I had brought, put on his thick horned rimmed tortoise shell glasses and began to read.

"You look very professorial," I said, feeling nervous. I was much more confident as a nurse. I knew diagnosis, I knew medicine, I knew nursing and I had done it for over 16 years. Hospitals, especially acute care hospitals, were my playing fields.

I sat silently for almost an hour as I watched him take his red felt pen and strike through my sentences, one after another. I wasn't near enough to see what he was doing but as he got closer to the bottom of the pile, I could feel my heart beating fast.

"I don't like poems," he said, as he picked up one of my pages. But I watched as he read one aloud and smiled.

I'll throw you a lifeline
A lasso of laughter
If you lay down
and let me love you.

"That's a good poem," he said.

"Thanks," I said. "But what about the stories?"

"I don't like to criticize another writer's work," he said. "A writer needs confidence just to keep going."

"I don't mind," I said. "I want to know."

"The greatest enemy of a writer is to begin to doubt the quality of his work," Mario said. "That's why I never show my books to anyone before they're finished."

"You want me to just sit here with you then turn around and go home. You expect me to just look at all those red lines and try to figure out what I did wrong?" I asked. "Instead of telling me what you think so I can learn?"

He looked up at me, over his glasses, studying me. "Move over here," he said. "I'll tell you if you want to know. But I won't be responsible if you get discouraged."

"Deal," I said. "But I want to know first. Do I have what it takes?"

Mario leaned back in his chair again and lit the biggest cigar I had ever seen. Long and dark. Then he began to blow smoke in big puffs as he looked toward the ceiling.

I sat in my chair, holding my breath, waiting. My imagination went wild. I had visions of him covering his eyes and his ears. What if my writing was really awful? Adolescent? Oh, God, I thought, I hate looking foolish, I hate not knowing.

Suddenly, I was acutely aware of all the holes in my education. I had never taken even one formal literature course in school. Aside from the nonfiction course I had just taken, I had never studied any kind of writing. For the last 16 years, since I'd become a nurse, I'd been reading medical journals. Catching a dread disease in a hospital didn't frighten me, but hearing what Mario had to say suddenly terrified me.

"Say something?" I pleaded. "I'm feeling very Victorian. I'm getting the vapors."

"You've got talent," he said, and then there was another long period of silence.

"What does that mean?" I asked. "Does it mean my stories are good?"

Mario was deep in thought. "You've got a good ear for dialogue, and raw talent," he said. "What you need to learn is the carpentry of writing."

"Carpentry?" I repeated.

"Writing can't be taught but it can be learned," he explained. "Carpentry is the nuts and bolts of writing."

"Do you know a good carpenter who would consider an apprentice? I asked, "I'm a quick study."

"Sure," he said, "I'm the greatest teacher in the Western Hemisphere." Then he began to laugh. "That's a joke," he said, self-consciously

"Why?" I asked.

"Because when I went up to Paramount for my first meeting, and they asked me if I wanted to write The Godfather screenplay, I asked how much money they were willing to pay. They told me first I had to write "a treatment." But I was young then and very arrogant about my writing. I told them I got paid to think. Unless they gave me money, I couldn't think. Then one of the smart young guys at the meeting asked why they should hire me. I got mad, so I told him "Because I am the greatest screenplay writer in the Western Hemisphere."

"Were you?" I asked.

"I had never written a screenplay in my life before The Godfather," he said, smiling, "but that's what confidence can do for you. And desperation. Fortunately, it worked out."

Chapter 5

It took six months more to wrap up my marriage. During that six months, Ned and I really tried to make it work. We talked, and fought and struggled with ourselves and each other to try to find a solution to our unhappiness. But the trouble was we were mismatched cogs in a crooked wheel and our marriage was a really rocky road.

Ned kept telling me that marriage offered safety but there were some trade-offs. "I don't feel safer," I told him.

"Kids do better as part of a family," he tried to convince me.

"We were a family, even before you," I told him.

At home, Ned and I kept trying to plow through all our solid beliefs about what a marriage should be. We did try to make allowances for each other, and accept each other, but it was an enormous effort for both of us. As he got more frightened, he got more rigid, and I got more frustrated.

My kids were teenagers, and so both were impossible anyway. But Ned would make a rule that I thought was ridiculous, like "I want the kids and their friends to come in and go out of the back door," and I would say, "That sounds like sit at the back of the bus. Unless all of us are going to do it, why should they?" Of course, once there isn't a united front, the kids always play one parent against another so it was inevitable. Teri, my sixteen year old, who resented rules in general, would break it. More problems. Ned and I would fight. Danny, my thirteen year old, began to cut school, and had to be grounded, but I was tired of fighting with him and someone had to enforce the punishment, so Ned became the executioner.

As long as I didn't try to talk to Ned about anything serious, or ask him for what I needed, we were fine, but once I tried to move closer to him, and take the conversation to deeper more intimate levels, he'd bolt like a frightened stallion.

Sometimes we got along even better than we had before I'd met Mario—there were moments of real intimacy—but he couldn't maintain a relationship without trying to control everything, and I couldn't allow that which turned me into a screaming maniac in order to "defend myself."

My best friends were a gang of nurses who met each Thursday night at my house to discuss what we'd need to do to change the world. We had been doing that for at least 15 years. It always started with the changes that needed to be made in the Health Care System and how we could better serve our patients, but it always got around to men. Each of us had at least one that we were struggling to deal fairly with, without sacrificing ourselves completely, or having our marriage bed turned into a bed of nails.

It was on one of those Thursday nights that I told the girls that Ned and I were trying to hang it together but it didn't look good. It was making both of us miserable most of the time. Ned kept saying I reminded him of Annie Hall, and he reminded me of Bluebeard.

Bridie, Maureen and Wanda had all met Mario when we were taking care of Erika and they liked him, but still he was a man, a famous one at that, so they were wary. Eventually, we again got around to the state of my marriage and to me moaning over my poor kids who were going to have to endure another divorce if we couldn't make it better.

"What's happened since we last met?" Maureen asked. She had bright blue eyes and dark short hair, and a lip that quivered when she got nervous.

"I was trying to maintain the status quo," I said. "I'm trying not to rock the boat any more. I made up my mind to work, write, and keep Mario as a friend. In other words, I'm trying to compromise."

Wanda had the greatest laugh in the world. She was shorter and blond and a little hard of hearing. But this she heard, and laughed. "Compromise? Status quo? You're funny," she said.

Wanda had left her husband—another "good man"—after she had been the perfect wife and mother for 15 years. But by then she was used up, nothing could stop her, she'd had it. So even if I could fool myself about my endurance, I couldn't fool Wanda.

Bridie was my craziest friend and goodness seeded her bones. From Ireland, she came to the US and married a Jewish man named Bernstein, then went to nursing school. She never lost her brogue, and always kept her Irish sense of humor. We met at the hospital and stayed friends for years. Now, she said simply, "You can't stay in a marriage once you're finished."

"Why?" I asked. "To save the kids, lots of women stay in marriages that they supplement."

"You make that sound nutritional," Bridie said. "Besides, you're not one of those women."

"What does that mean?" I asked, frowning at her.

"Women like you and me are good at a lot of things, in fact better than most in many things. But marriage isn't one of them. Compromise isn't one of them. Plus, you have this annoying habit of having to tell the truth. That always dooms a marriage. That and any sense of justice, fairness or equality."

"Oh God," I said to her that night. "You sound like a bitter witch, my love. You have fallen from grace and have lost your way. Did you never believe in Princes?"

"Princes had their own kingdoms and their own slaves," she explained. "Besides, you're mixing realties. Did you ever hear of a fairy tale called 'The Prince and His Wife' or 'The Princess and her husband?'"

My friends told me, they tried to warn me, but I didn't listen. I couldn't hear.

Destiny has a way of pushing just the right buttons when evolution calls to demand change. A couple of days later Fate stepped right into the center of my life, right into my kitchen. To this day

I swear my marriage might have survived all the little injuries, even some of the big hurts, if it wasn't for that one unforgivable incident.

That afternoon, Ned was in his office with a patient trying to help her straighten out her life so she could be happy.

I was hungry. And unsuspecting. Naively, I went into the refrigerator to grab the mayo to make myself a sandwich.

The jar I pulled out said "Hellmann's" but the color was wrong—a fake too yellow. I unscrewed the top and smelled it. I hesitated and smelled it again—it smelled a little different. Not bad, just different. Not sure of my perceptions, and not wanting to drop dead in the middle of the afternoon in my kitchen while Ned was busy, I stuck my finger in the jar and tasted it. And there it was! Different. I was just about to pick up the phone to call the company to complain about their new recipe, when Ned walked in and saw the whole jar of mayo in the garbage.

"What happened?" he asked. "Why did you throw the mayo out?"

"I think they changed the recipe. I'm going to call the company," I told him. "That's the third jar this month that's been bad."

Ned started to speak, and then in the middle of a sentence, he stopped.

"What?" I asked. "Please don't do that. Don't start a sentence and then just leave me wondering."

Ned just shook his head, but I knew something was wrong. He looked guilty. "Did you taste it?" he asked.

"Yes," I said. "I did, and it's a little off. It doesn't taste like Hellmann's."

"I can't tell the difference," he said.

"If I couldn't, that would be fine," I said. "But they've changed something and I want them to know, it's been noticed. I don't like it."

"I would have sworn you couldn't tell," he said. "I was sure it was hype and you were being fooled by the advertisers."

"There's a sentence in between those two thoughts, you've left out," I said, laughing. "Or I'm not as smart as I used to be."

Ned stared at me for a few seconds, and then he shook his head. "I switched the mayo from a store brand jar because I really believed you wouldn't know the difference," he said.

"You're kidding, right? You mean you deliberately tried to trick me?" I asked, stricken. "You know how scary it is for me when someone plays with my perceptions. What were you trying to do?"

"No," he said. "I was doing an experiment. I was trying to prove that the power of advertising can sway public opinion. More important, I was saving us money."

"Ned," I said. "How many times have I told you that my biggest vulnerability is my perceptions? How can I trust you if you're going to play with them?"

"Look," he said. "Don't get crazy on me. I switched the bread a couple of times, and the shampoo and you never noticed. I even switched the Scotch."

In that moment I dropped out of one world and into another. "I don't drink Scotch," I told him. "I haven't been eating bread. But now you've ruined everything. How can I ever trust you again?"

"But you want me to trust you?" he asked.

"No Ned," I said. "I don't. I may not give you what you want, but I wouldn't lie to you and pretend you were getting it. One would make you not trust me, but the other would make you not trust yourself. That is so much worse, I can't even begin to explain it."

Ned lowered his head as he listened to me but then he asked, "Is there anything I can to do now to make it up to you?"

"Not at all," I said. "I'm done. I'm really finished, no matter what else happens, this isn't working for me anymore."

When anyone asks why my second marriage broke up, I always tell them, "It was because of Hellman's mayonnaise.

I cried, Ned cried, we split. It took almost a year of us trying to disconnect and put our lives back into some kind of separate order, but the kids were amazingly okay. Ned moved around the block and my sister Bibs with her two kids moved into the house.

My mom and dad didn't say much though now they came to visit every evening. After a month, they knew it would do no good to try to convince me to save a broken marriage. My mind was hard to change once I'd made any decision. "A life of quiet desperation doesn't suit me," was all I said to my father one evening.

"Well, then, make your house your home," he said. "And take care of your family."

Chapter 6

After the split, I worked nights and spent a lot of my days at home writing pages and stories for my book. I was truly passionate about nursing and about my hero patients. But, like soldiers who go to war to save a country, but are totally unprepared for the wreckage and the bodies that are blowing up around them, telling the stories I had to tell, triggered memories in me that caused PTSD. There is no way to tell the stories of heroes without showing the demons they had to face and try to destroy. Reliving it was much harder than I imagined it would be.

The rest of the time I spent with my kids, talking to them, trying to get Danny who was 15 to go to school, to stay in school, and then to do some homework. That was pretty much a losing battle.

My daughter Teri left for California to attend a state College there and worked at a battered woman's shelter. We spoke for hours on the phone each week. Mostly I kept warning her, "Beware of the Moonies. Don't get on any buses."

All she kept saying was, "I'm so glad to be independent. It feels so right here."

Life seemed to be moving forward in spite of my guilt.

My mother and father began to visit each night after dinner, and my sister Bibs and her kids, Jenny and Chris, who were 4 and 7—settled in to the other side of my house and so our lives continued with, "A family is..."

Mario and I saw each other on weekends and sometimes I'd go over his house on Wednesday nights before work to cook him dinner unless we felt like going out to eat.

The rest of the time, his kids were there making his house a home.

But it wasn't long before Mario got restless, and I noticed a big difference between us. Mario couldn't stay in any one place for more than a month without growing wings, and I was pretty much rooted in place. Our first negotiations had to begin.

"I thought you said you wanted to travel and see the world," he said one night after dinner.

"I do," I admitted. "I want to travel and learn. I want to stand where Socrates stood, and walk where Jesus did. Maybe even visit a leper colony like Padre Pia."

"Another perfectly decent woman ruined by religion," he said.

"You don't like Socrates?" I asked. "I know you don't believe in Jesus, but what about visiting The Holy Land?"

"I like places where I can gamble," he said.

"You're right," I said. "I don't believe there's gambling in the Holy Land. I don't know about Greece. The Leper colony is a personal thing, because I've just always loved the Lives of Saints."

"It's a definite 'no' to the Leper Colony," he said, deadpan. "I won't change my mind about that. You'll have to go with your friends."

"Maybe the whole idea of traveling is another romantic ideal," I said. "Maybe I won't like it as much as I thought I would. Maybe dreams should just stay dreams."

Mario laughed. "As someone once said, 'more tears are shed over answered prayers than unanswered prayers.'"

"We'll see," I said. "Maybe I'll love it. Who knows?"

It was long after Erika died and enough time after I'd gotten divorced, that Mario asked me if I wanted to come with him to Malibu. Each year he went to 'hang out' where the work was for screenplays, that's where he met those who would offer him 'a piece of the action' because everyone in Hollywood was always working on pitching a new "project."

It was in Malibu that people came to see him, people who could "Green Light" a project. None of the big players in the movie business came to New York at that time. They were all in California.

Mario and I were sitting on the couch in his study when he invited me. "This year I'm renting William Wyler's house," he told me. "Should be fun. Want to come?"

I hesitated for a couple of minutes before I answered. "I don't know who William Wyler is," I admitted.

"He's one of the great Directors," Mario explained. "He did movies like 'The Little Foxes,' 'Mrs. Miniver' and 'The Best Years of our Lives.' They're classics."

I admitted I had never seen them.

"That's another reason not to date younger women," Mario said, resting on the couch in his study. "You find you have nothing in common. You can't talk about the things that interest you. They have no idea what you mean."

"So, why would you?" I asked. "Why would any man?"

"A young woman has energy," he said. "And a certain kind of aesthetic beauty that appeals to an artist's sensibility. They're still new—like babies, because life hasn't worn them down yet—they still have enthusiasm and hope for life."

"For men, young women are a shield against death?" I asked.

"You could put it that way," he said. "Or you could say they're cheerful."

"Didn't William Wyler make any movies I would know?" I asked.

"Roman Holiday with Audrey Hepburn," he asked. "Because of your good Catholic upbringing, I have no doubt you've seen 'Ben Hur.'"

"Yes" I said. "I've seen those old movies, but he didn't direct anything newer?"

Mario was silent for a few minutes. Finally, he said, "The Collector? And—Funny Girl."

"Barbara Streisand?" I said, with more excitement. "Mario, I don't think I know what a director is or does."

"A novelist writes a book. He's in control until an editor gets it. But the director is the boss of the movie," Mario explained. "He runs everything. That's why I tell everyone The Godfather was Francis Coppola's movie."

"But if you didn't write the book," I said, "he couldn't have made the movie."

"True," he said. "The author of the book and the screenplay is given credit for the story. But the movies are a visual medium and putting it up on the screen is the director's gift. So, he gets the credit or takes the blame for what the audience sees."

"You should still get more credit for those movies," I said, stubbornly. "Those characters are your creation. They came straight out of the book."

"You live and die by casting," Mario explained. "Without Francis' fighting for Brando and Pacino, it would never have been the movie it was."

"What does that mean?" I asked. "You didn't choose Brando?"

"I did," he said. "I even wrote him a letter to ask him if he would do it, and he called me. It was Brando who told me that I had to get the Director to fight for him. And Francis did. Brando is a genius actor, but Francis is a genius director."

"A writer has no say in a movie?" I asked.

Mario shook his head. "Very little," he said. "That's why I'm grateful to Francis," he said. "He put my book up on the screen and that rarely happens."

Chapter 7

When I flew to LA to stay with Mario that first time, I found him waiting in the gate with Lanetta, his West Coast personal assistant. He looked as happy to see me as I was to see him. But so did Lanetta, though I'd never met her before. She was so warm and welcoming that it felt as though we had known each other for years.

Mario had often talked about Lanetta. Still, I wasn't prepared for how pretty she was; young, thin, with shoulder length shiny dark hair and a great smile. She looked like an ad for healthy living. I should have hated her at first glance, but I didn't.

At the time, I had no clue what a personal assistant was. So, Mario explained how over the 13 years she'd worked with him, she was his right-hand girl. She made arrangements for everything. She set up his appointments, drove him everywhere, even bought clothes for him and his kids. She got Academy Award preview film tickets and the best theatre tickets. She booked flights, set up invitations and arranged to have Mario's Malibu business parties catered each Sunday. She also sent invitations to the "right" people so Mario was able to meet with directors and studio executives who could green light a project. Mario said she couldn't be considered a secretary because she didn't type. But she did know the right typists to hire.

She was the only woman I've ever met who could say "*Yes, Boss*" to any request he made, not lose status or power, and even look sincere. Mario swore she was not as innocent as she looked and that "Yes, Boss" was calculated to define their relationship so no one would get the wrong idea. When I asked him why he never fell in love with her, or slept with her, he told me she was more like one of his kids. "I'm not attracted to young women," he said. "In my view, a woman needs to have some troubles to overcome before she becomes interesting."

I sure had had enough "troubles" to qualify but I didn't mention that I was only 37 at the time. I just figured that in Hollywood that wasn't young.

The trip from Los Angeles along Pacific Coast Highway to Malibu was amazing. Beautiful people, slim and trim, all dressed in white shorts and sneakers ran alongside the road like exotic antelope. For a moment, I wondered if any of them shared the troubles that existed in the rest of the world.

Still, Malibu, the place, was nothing like I expected it to be. I'd pictured huge mansions on great estates, instead of beach houses so close together that they almost touched. Later I found out that when the windows were open you could hear conversations from one house to another.

William Wyler's house was a large contemporary cedar shake house right on Malibu Beach—so close to the water that the waves almost reached the patio when the tide rolled in. To anyone else it would have been terribly romantic, but it terrified me because I'd never been able to learn to swim.

Still, later that night, standing on the balcony of Wyler's house at sunset, watching the pink and orange sun go down over the horizon, I understood why Malibu was such a special place. The clear blue water, the great green hills, the tall mountains were all part of the beauty of the landscape. It was seductive and awe inspiring.

Across Pacific Coast Highway, across from the house, there was a small strip mall with a couple of ritzy restaurants, and of course a fresh food market. All the food in California seemed terribly clean and healthy to me. No Italian grease that I loved to eat at home.

Mario had a great writing setup at that Malibu house. His typewriter, an old black manual Underwood, was set up in the upstairs bedroom in front of the ceiling to floor windows which looked out right onto the beach. While he typed, I read and wrote some pages.

From where we sat, we could both watch the surf and imagine for hours. At night, the sound of those waves lulled us to sleep.

I learned a lot on that first trip, and I got a bunch of my own writing done too because Mario was pretty quiet and introspective. Whenever we were alone, I'd meditate, listen to tapes or write. The nights were so peaceful that we could only read or watch TV. I knew I should be thrilled to death surrounded by so much luxury but it was like an outfit that was too big or too small for me. And despite the insanity of it, I missed my kids.

We were at the Malibu house for about a week when Mario asked if I wanted to go with him to the Diet Center in Los Angeles. I imagined long walks over rolling hills and lots of space again—like a yoga retreat center.

Mario said having me with him would give him something to do between the lectures and the exercise sessions to keep his mind off eating, and the nurse in me immediately responded. "Sure, I've never been to LA." It sounded like a dream.

But as soon as I got there, I knew I was wrong. The Diet Center was housed in a red brick building, like any modern hospital complete with long sterile looking corridors. I had gotten used to the antiseptic smells in hospitals, and that fragrance held a certain excitement for me. But the smell in these corridors was different. Awful. That was the first thing I noticed. The second thing was that all the people I saw had grey skin. I hadn't seen that color grey since I'd worked in the Cardiac Units of Intensive Care. The nurse in me quickly began to diagnose, "Heart...no circulation. Could have been clogged arteries as all the speakers during the lectures Mario had to attend said, but I was pretty sure it also came from everyone holding their breath because of the funny smell.

While the rest of the building was Purgatory, the cafeteria was pure hell for my nose. Big heaps of steamed or boiled vegetables filled several stainless chafing dishes but these were not vegetables like carrots or string beans. No, that would have been too benign. These stainless serving trays were overflowing with overcooked cauliflower and broccoli. Everyone was encouraged to eat as much as they wanted.

The food they cooked may have been low fat, low sugar, low salt but it sure was high garlic and from the time I was a little kid, I couldn't stand the smell of garlic. An oddity for an Italian, I'll admit.

Each morning, before the lectures when Mario weighed in, he seemed to weigh the same weight. It took over 3 days before he lost a pound.

"It hardly seems worth it," he said, disappointed.

"I don't know why you want to get skinny. I like excess," I told him. "I'm the kind of girl who loves jumping into a huge pile of leaves. I like you the way you are."

On the other hand, I myself lost 5 pounds in the first 5 days, but that was because I couldn't eat a thing. "I know the basis of their beliefs," I told him. "But no matter all the scientific fancy talk, I know this is aversion therapy, and I swear I can starve you somewhere that smells better. Somewhere we can have fun and not have to wear masks so we can breathe."

The first week we attended several lectures, afterwards Mario tried to eat a lot of soup, broccoli and cauliflower. Then when he couldn't stand it another minute, we snuck out to Denny's Diner so he could get a cheeseburger. Unfortunately, Mario couldn't resist temptation and so he ordered pancakes too.

"Why are we staying at a Diet Center if you're going to cheat?" I asked.

"I always cheat when I go to a fat farm," he said. "But I always lose a few pounds. Besides, it makes me feel virtuous."

Though I really tried to keep my lips sealed so as not to discourage him, Mario could tell I didn't like it there.

"I have to give it a reasonable try," Mario insisted. "I have to lose a few more pounds. I've already lost 5, so it works. It will add years to my life. My whole family has a history of heart disease."

"But I'll bet they enjoyed the food they ate," I said. "I'd rather enjoy eating and die young. Still, if this is your journey to health, I'm all for it. For you."

Yet, surprising things come out of even awful experiences and on the second week we were there, as Mario slept and dreamed, he suddenly jumped out of bed, ran over to the desk and began to scribble madly.

'What? What?" I asked. But he just continued to scribble.

Finally, after an hour or so, he looked up from his pages, got back into bed, and said, "That's it."

"What?" I asked.

"The next book I have to write," he said.

"What is it?"

"A book about a young idealistic politician like a Kennedy, who becomes president, and who with the best of intentions becomes a fascist dictator. I'll call it "The Last K.""

"Interesting," I said. "Hard for me to imagine, but interesting nevertheless."

But as I thought about it, I was concerned. "Aren't you worried that the Kennedys will come down on you and stop that publication? Can't you be sued or worse?"

Mario raised his eyebrows when he looked at me. "I'm the guy who wrote about the Mafia," he said. "I can't worry about everything or I'd never write anything worth writing. It's the abuse of power in any system, human nature and the human condition that's worth exploring, or what's the reason to be a writer? Besides, The Godfather wasn't only a family story, it was really about the capitalist system, and business."

"But why pick one of the most powerful families in America?" I asked.

"It's not a huge jump," Mario explained. "Everyone thinks that a fascist President in America is an impossibility, but that's not so. It's an American arrogance. Given human nature, it can happen anywhere and given human greed and the need for power, it can happen in no time." He snapped his fingers for emphasis.

Somehow, we fell back to sleep, and I actually dreamed about the stories I was writing for my own book.

In the morning, Mario called Lanetta, and told her to book two tickets to Vegas the following day. "Time to have some fun," he announced. "We've been working too hard. I need some balance, some fun. Then I can go home to begin to work. I'm a happy man when I write. When I don't, I'm miserable."

"I can see that," I said.

"Not well enough yet," he told me smiling. "You're still more the nurse than the writer. When you become more the writer than the nurse, then you'll understand."

It was during that trip that I first learned something about the process of writing, but even more, how much courage I'd have to have as a writer to believe in myself when I really needed to tell the truth.

Chapter 8

Early the following morning we hopped a small plane and took off for Vegas.

I wanted to see "sin city" because it was edgy but I was also sort of nervous not knowing what to expect.

When we landed, the Sands had sent a limo to pick us up at the airport. The driver held a huge sign "PUZO" that we could see as we walked toward the baggage claim.

"So much for anonymity," I said.

Mario just smiled. He was already feeling free and planning on having fun.

But as we rode down the strip to the Sands Hotel and Casino, Mario seemed disappointed. He said it wasn't as dramatic as he hoped it would be because it was daytime and there was none of the glitz and flash of the neon skyline. Even so, that day he was more animated than I'd ever seen him.

He told me stories, complete with waving hands, about his first trip to Vegas....

"When I first saw it, this city was the most magical place in the world," Mario said. "Every building was covered with bright lights, beautiful young girls with scant outfits pranced around the casino and sat at every table. There were buffet tables of rich feasts in every restaurant and you could eat as much as you wanted, because it was all comped." A hedonist's dream.

"Comped?" I asked.

"Free," Mario explained. "Complementary. The casino picks up the tab for Room and Board for any of the high rollers—guys who gamble for big stakes."

"There were huge buffets in every casino on the Strip. When you got up in the morning you could walk downstairs or along the streets and have steak, eggs, sausage and pancakes for $1.95. There were big trays of biscuits, pots of whipped cream, oatmeal, cream of wheat, and steaming carafes of coffee or tea alongside tall glass pitchers of freshly squeezed orange juice—all you could drink."

The Sands Hotel was Mario's favorite. It was only a short ride to the casino and when we arrived it was obvious that everyone on staff knew Mario. The bellboys all called him "Mr. P and saluted as they smiled. They greeted him like a long lost relative. Without any discomfort they called me, Mrs. P. and I felt like a kid pretending to be someone else.

That day the bellboy immediately took us up the elevator to the penthouse—the best place to be because of the view. But as luxurious as the suite was, I was afraid of the tower.

"Mario, can't we stay on the 3rd floor?" I asked him. "That way if there's a fire, we can always jump."

Mario looked at me and laughed. He was gracious enough not to point out that whether I had to jump from the third floor or the fifteenth, I wasn't going to land intact. Instead he said, "Why don't we just ask for a suite in the cottages in back. On the ground floor," he said. "That way we can just walk outside if there's a fire."

"I'm not kidding," I said. "You know it's because of the burn unit...."

He hugged me. "I know. No problem," he said. "We'll stay in a cottage."

Once we put our suitcases in our new suite, which was just as big, and just as lush and glitzy, Mario rubbed his hands together and announced we were ready to go gambling. But I was starved. "Could we get a little something to eat first?" I asked.

"Anything, my dear," he said. Mario was in his glory in Vegas, he was even chatty, and smiling—a truly happy man. But that was before he started gambling.

The first thing that struck me as we walked through the dimly lit crowded casinos on our way to the coffee shop was that there were no windows or clocks. Those rooms were secret chambers, severed from the outside world. Inside, bathed in a neon daylight, there was no sense of time, only an air of nervous excitement and the sound of spilling coins. The ringing bells from the winning slot machines rang out almost constantly and the shouts of victory from the lucky players filled the air with adrenaline.

"Mario, when do they start pumping oxygen into the casino?" I asked.

Mario looked puzzled.

"Fools Die," I reminded him. "I read it in your book."

Mario laughed. "Fiction, my dear," he said. "Pure fiction."

The coffee shop was large and circular with huge skylights and walls of clear glass through which we could see out onto the small two story stucco cottages behind.

Mario and I sat in a cozy booth on dark green leather benches and looked outside. The several kidney shaped swimming pools in front of those cottages were full of young men and women splashing and playing joyfully under the hot Nevada sun. The children seemed happy and carefree as they ran around the perfectly manicured lawn and jumped into those pools.

When the cocktail waitress came up to us, she smiled at Mario and asked, "The usual coffee and pancakes?"

"Sure, sounds good," he said. "They have the best pancakes here."

The waitress turned to me and said, "You should try the buffet."

"Go ahead," Mario said. "I'll have some of the fresh fruit."

I had never seen a more lavish buffet. Silver tureens of fresh strawberries, melon balls and pineapple slices filled the buffet tables covered with starched white tablecloths. On fine china trays and silver platters there were dainty croissants and turnovers surrounded by small jars of honey and preserves; sterling serving trays rested on Bunsen burners and overflowed with sausage and eggs both scrambled and benedict. Everything I had ever tasted or imagined was on that table. All of it looked as though it had just been picked from the orchards, freshly cut and arranged in intricate designs.

I lifted a white china plate and placed a ton of breakfast foods on it.

Mario seemed in no hurry to reach the casino, and so we had a lazy breakfast. I was really enjoying the warm Nevada sunshine coming through the large coffee house windows. It had been freezing in New York when I left and even in Malibu the weather wasn't as warm.

When we finally finished breakfast, Mario rubbed his hands together happily and said, "Okay, now to do battle. I feel lucky!" I was nervous because I knew nothing about gambling. "Let's try roulette first," Mario said. "Just watch me and do the same thing with your own numbers."

"Good God," I said. "I'm scared to death. It's a hedonist's heaven, no place for a wanna be saint."

Mario laughed as he moved more quickly toward the sound of the thousand lucky coins spilling out of the slot machines, while the flashing lights above those machines spotlighted the next lucky winner.

Still, I was on sensory overload. It reminded me of the Medical Center's Intensive Care Unit with all the monitors going off at once.

At the cashier's cage, Mario gave me some colored chips and said, "Start with dollar chips, if you get lucky you can get fives at the table."

"Five dollars on each number?" I said. "We'll be broke in no time."

"Unless, we're lucky," he said.

"What kind of chips are those?" I asked pointing to the black ones he had just gotten from the cashier.

"Hundreds," he said.

"We're going to go to hell," I told him.

"I don't believe in Hell," he said.

Mario was moving fast and I quickly ran after him trying not to drop my chips out of the red plastic holder.

Before I knew it, we were standing at one of the roulette tables and Mario was leaning over placing his bets. "Morning Mr. P," the tuxedo dressed croupier said from behind a glass shield at the head of the table. Mario was chewing on a cigar, so he nodded a greeting but said nothing. He was concentrating intently as he placed his bets.

"How many do you put down at each spin?" I asked.

"Watch," he mumbled. "Just watch..." He meant don't speak.

I took a step back behind Mario, because other gamblers were pushing to get around the table but my eyes studied everything he was doing. Suddenly the air in the room seemed to shift and I felt light headed. Mario began to move in a surrealistic dance deftly placing several chips on each number. He was completely focused. In the Zone. I was completely off balance. My perceptions shifted. Mario was moving with grace and certainty as he placed a pile of chips on each number. Then as the croupier spun the wheel and the ball bounced from one slot to another, Mario stood statue still, watching—silent.

The ball landed on a number Mario hadn't bet. He never blinked.

I almost had a heart attack as I watched the croupier sweep the hundred dollar chips off the green felt of the table. I thought of all the starving children in the world. I began to say something but again Mario was too focused for me to interrupt him. More black chips.

"Twice as many?" I asked.

"Doubling up," he said, as though I knew what that meant.

He doubled up three more times before he hit, but when he hit, he won thousands of dollars. He hit his numbers several times and then he lost. One more spin and he stopped playing. "Okay, we're even. Let's get out of here before they steal my money back," he said.

My chips were still in my blazer pockets. "Should I play these?" I said, but he was already walking fast, leaving the casino.

When I caught up with him, he said, "Got to leave while you're ahead. Once your streak is over, every minute you stay at the tables costs you money."

"What should we do with these?" I asked him holding out a few chips.

"Keep them," he told me. "After we take a nap, we'll try again. Maybe you'll get lucky."

Those chips were days' pay as a nurse. I didn't really want to just throw them away. "What if I lose it all?" I asked.

"Then you figure it's not your lucky day," he said. "We'll try again, tomorrow."

"With what?" I asked.

"I'll give you another two hundred," he said. "That's your stake. Have fun with it. Play."

Mario lost on that trip, but I won and we had fun. We had been in Vegas for two days and when we left, Mario considered it a big success. We were almost even.

I was enormously relieved that we could get away from the tension, the crowds of people, and all the noise. But there were more surprises to come.

Chapter 9

The day we got back from Vegas, Lanetta handed us an invitation for a party at Valerie Harper's house which was about a mile and a half up Malibu beach. I didn't want to go, or more to the point, parties weren't my strength.

"Oh my God," I said. "I can't go to a party with people who I'm supposed to know, but won't. I've spent too many years working in hospitals and raising kids. I can't even remember the last movie I saw."

Lanetta reassured me, but Mario just looked at me. "Parties are places you can meet the people who might one day ask you to write a screenplay. Or ask you about your book," he said. "I thought you wanted to be a writer…"

"I'm not good at this," I said. "I don't have a book yet. I don't plan to write screenplays. And I certainly don't have a clue what to wear."

"Lanetta will take you shopping tomorrow," he said. "We'll go to Rodeo Drive. You'll find something."

"Oh Mario," I moaned. "I hate this."

"I know," he said, smiling at me. "But sometimes you have to do things you don't want to in order to be a success."

"I thought you said you didn't do things you didn't want to," I said.

Mario nodded. "Sure, I said that. But if I had done those things, I would have been successful a lot earlier."

"So now you do?" I asked.

"No, he said. "No matter what happens, people usually do what they want to do."

Lanetta reassured me. "We'll have fun shopping," she said. "Then we can have lunch someplace famous."

"Thanks," I said. "But we'll have to sit in a booth in the back so no one will see us."

"Certainly, my dear," Mario said.

The following day, Lanetta came to pick us up. It was a beautiful sunny day and as we walked down the street and looked into all the store windows, I thought how 'high class' everything looked. I couldn't see myself wearing any of those clothes.

Mario and Lanetta encouraged me to look inside a few stores and in the end we drifted into Gucci's. This was no department store. They had couches, and coffee tables and waiters who brought drinks for the men while the ladies shopped. Egads!! Mario looked at all the jewelry cases before he sat on the couch to read. By the time I saw him again, he had chosen about a dozen Gucci watches to give his family as gifts. He handed me the one he'd bought for me.

"Thank you so much," I said. "You shouldn't have."

Mario looked at me. "You don't like it?" He never waited for me to answer, he just said, "Run over there and get the one you want."

"Oh, no," I objected. "I sort of really like this one, because you gave it to me."

'What are you trying to say?" he asked.

"I like leather bands," I said.

He looked at Lanetta, then he got up and walked over to the fashionably dressed salesperson. Within minutes he was back with my watch and another with a red leather band."

I really loved it. "Thank you so much," I said. "I really am crazy about it."

"Good," he said. "Look around and see what else you like.."

I protested at first, but in order to please him, I began to look around. On one of the shelves I saw a pair of boots I really liked. But I was sure they wouldn't be my size.

Lanetta walked over the salesperson and asked about them.

"The soft blue leather ostrich?" the salesman asked.

"Yes," I told him. "In size 4 or even 5." I turned to Lanetta and said, "At home in New York its cold enough to wear thick socks so I can get away with the 5's." I was certain they wouldn't have a pair that fit.

When the salesperson came out with a four and a half, I almost died of shock. I was tickled to death. When I put them on I felt like Cinderella.

"Oh, my God, I love these," I said, and suddenly Mario was standing right there.

He turned to the salesman. "Wrap them up for the lady," he said.

I was so excited that I threw myself on him and hugged him. But he gently pulled my arms down from around his neck and held my hand. By his expression, I knew I had embarrassed him.

"Sorry," I said. "But I love them to death."

Mario laughed. "Look around. Anything else you'd like? They have pocketbooks over there and wallets if you like."

"I'm good," I said. "Shouldn't we ask how much my boots are?"

Just then Lanetta offered to take me outside to look at a few other stores while Mario paid for them, but I was feeling grateful and wanted to wait with him, so I refused.

"What initials do you wish on your bag, Madame?" the young man asked.

I frowned and looked at Mario. "What is he asking me?"

"Lanetta chose a matching bag for you, and they're going to monogram it for you," Mario explained.

Once we were finished, Mario handed me the receipt and said, "Keep this in case you and Lanetta have to come back and change anything."

We met Lanetta outside and began to walk to the restaurant for lunch. That's when I looked at the receipt. $1800 dollars for the boots, and $1500 for the pocketbook. I almost passed out cold. I had no idea boots could cost that much or I never could have let Mario buy them for me. In my head all I could see was all the starving people in the world. I was so stunned, I was actually silent.

By the time we got back to Malibu, I had decided on something from my own closet. I chose a navy and white nautical outfit I'd brought from New York. But if I could have found a hair shirt—like the ones those old neurotic monks wore for penance—I would have thrown that on instead.

The following week when it was time to go to Valerie Harper's party, I was over my guilt and determined to have a good time, or at least not to make Mario uncomfortable. After all, it was a business meeting of sorts, and I could learn more about writers and movie-makers. If I was successful, I would need it. And business—including parties—was one of the reasons why Mario came out to Malibu.

Valerie Harper opened the door to her house and let us in. She was prettier in person, as real as she was as Rhoda, in the Mary Tyler Moore show, as funny and charming. Within minutes of us following her up the stairs she told me her mother had been a nurse, and for fun that night, they were having a psychic tarot card read for any of us who wanted it. She showed me the room the turbaned psychic was sitting in, complete with colored crystal ball, and then just told me to make myself comfortable.

I smiled and refused the psychic, and then both Mario and I followed Valerie into a large open living room filled with people. There were couples sitting in clusters all around and she led us to a conversation pit and introduced us. "Mario and Carol," she told them smiling. "This is Neil, and Marsha." She introduced us to many more people but I only remember Neil and Marsha.

Sitting down on the white couches next to them, Mario and Neil began to speak. I was looking around terrified that a famous person would walk over to meet Mario and I'd be completely embarrassed because I didn't recognize them.

Suddenly, Marsha turned to me and asked, "Are you an actress?"

I smiled back and said, "No, I'm a nurse. What do you do?"

Before she had a chance to answer, Mario got up, grabbed my hand and dragged me away. "What's up?" I asked.

"I need some fresh air," he said. "I want to show you the sunset. Sunsets are beautiful here."

"Okay," I said. A waiter approached and asked if I wanted some coke, and I said, "No thanks, I'd rather have ginger ale."

Mario threw me a look but didn't say anything.

Outside on the balcony, the red sun was going down, falling into a purple skyline. Birds flew like black cut—out shadows against the orange sunset.

"By the way," Mario said. "Marsha and Neil? That was Marsha Mason and Neil Simon."

I'm sure my eyes showed what I felt. Even I recognized those names. "Oh, my God," I said, and covered my face. "I've seen her in movies. But I didn't recognize her. I asked her what she did."

"What did she say?" Mario asked. He seemed quite amused but I was so humiliated I felt like crying.

Mario put his arm around my shoulder and pulled me close as we both stared out over the water. "Isn't this the most beautiful sunset you've ever seen?" Mario asked.

"Isn't it the same damn sunset we have in Amityville?" I said, but I couldn't make it work. I couldn't stop the tears from running down my cheeks. "Please take me home?" I asked Mario. "Please?"

Mario managed to get us out of there without too much of a fuss saying I had a migraine headache. I wanted so much to thank Valerie Harper for being so real, and so welcoming, but more than that, I wanted to apologize to Marsha Mason for not recognizing her.

I couldn't because that night, I was completely out of my league and I felt the wolves chasing at my heels.

Returning home to Long Island, after our whirlwind trip to Santa Monica, Malibu and Vegas was like dropping out of the sky and landing back on earth. Safe. One of Mario's sons picked us up at the airport, and drove me home where everyone was waiting to greet me.

It was so great being home again that my friends, family and I stayed awake talking till late into the night. I felt good, I was happy again.

The following morning, I got up early, anxious to begin writing again. I went into my study and went through the huge piles of mail on my desk but before too long I lost patience with it, and began to look through my pages. I really had so much I wanted to write.

I had taken a break from nursing for a few months and was doing some projects for Mario. I had researched Coney Island for an article he wrote and I was writing some other articles for nursing journals and even one on mercy killing in hospitals for New York Magazine under a pseudonym of Teri Daniels.

Now, most days I spent hours just writing the "pieces" for my book. I started with the patients that were still so clear in my mind that it was easy to describe them and even easier to rant about the injustices of life and especially in medicine.

Mario and I developed a schedule that worked for us. Both of us needed time to ourselves, both of us were happy with our own lives. Neither of us wanted more then. We were both happy to get home after having lived together on our trips.

But Mario and I were just getting to know each other. It was only a few months before Mario got restless and wanted to travel again.

Chapter 10

The first time Mario took me to Cannes, for the film festival, I hated it. As soon as we landed at the airport in France, large groups of people who seemed to know each other, swarmed around us. So many people came over to greet Mario that I felt like an extra at a class reunion.

It was uncomfortable because there was no way to introduce me and make me feel okay about it. First Mario tried, "My friend, Carol." But when he looked at me, and I frowned, he quickly added, "My girlfriend, Carol."

"Oh God," I moaned. "We're almost a hundred years old. You can't say girlfriend."

Mario nodded and I went to wait for the suitcases at the baggage carousel.

When I saw them, I called to Mario. But he was deep in conversation with several young men he apparently knew.

I walked over to them, nodded and smiled. Mario reached for my hand and introduced me, "This is my paramour." They barely noticed, but I almost fainted, and as they turned to go, Mario turned to me and whispered, "What?"

"How would you feel if I introduced you as my gigolo?"

Mario frowned now. "Well, how do you want to be introduced? My companion or my significant other?"

"No that makes me feel like your nurse," I said. "My buddy, my partner, something that sort of explains us. You're the wordsmith, think of something." But I had no other suggestions, and by now, I just wanted to escape as quickly as possible.

By the time Mario got a porter to carry the bags to the car, a young woman with blond hair, young, pretty, and breathless with excitement, came up to Mario and asked, "Hey, Mario, can I hitch a ride with you into town. I can't seem to get a taxi."

"Sorry," he said. "There's no room." This time, he didn't introduce me.

Now I was really upset.

"What's wrong now?" he asked me.

"You slept with her," I said. "Or you would have introduced me."

"How?" he asked, furiously chewing on his cigar. He was as pissed as I was.

"Maybe as Carol," I said. "Maybe just by my name. No credentials."

He didn't speak for several minutes. "I wanted you to have a good time. I wanted you to see the French Riviera and maybe even have fun hanging out with some stars. I thought you'd enjoy a vacation away from all your responsibilities."

"And my family?" I said. "People I enjoy being with? People I belong with and my friends who I have something in common with. I hate it here."

Mario didn't say anything for a long time, a scary silence. Then finally he asked, "Are you going to keep being a pain in the ass or are you going to try to have a good time as long as we're here?"

"You don't understand why I'm upset, right?" I asked.

"Sure, I do," he said. "But I'm not responsible for the entire English language."

"Well, I just hate that only a title like 'wife' has any status in this damn culture," I said.

"That's because it has so few benefits," Mario said, smiling. "Don't you get it? It's a trick. As soon as women find out what a rip off marriage is, they won't even want it. It's a thankless job and a archaic concept especially for an independent woman."

We stayed at the beautiful Grand Hotel in an elegant suite with a balcony overlooking the deep blue Mediterranean. Sailboats dotted the water, their different colored flags flying in the breeze making a colorful panorama. It really did feel like a celebration.

That night as Mario and I walked along the crowded brightly lit sidewalks on our way to a restaurant, with the sights and sounds of a street fair all around us, I felt good. There were artists painting in bright colored oils on wooden easels, vendors with long velvet covered tables selling jewelry, and people formally dressed for nightlife.

Suddenly, a darkly dressed and veiled group of gypsy women moved through the crowd like swarming blackbirds and encircled us. One woman unfurled her cape showing a dark eyed infant sucking his thumb. Several of the others held their hands out. Everything changed.

Mario grabbed my elbow and shook his head, pushing us through them, back into the fast moving crowd of glamorous well-dressed people.

"We could have given them some money," I said.

But Mario looked angry. "Don't pull any money out here," he said. "You'll make yourself a target."

"What kind of fairy tale is this?" I asked as we walked quickly toward the restaurant.

"Grimm's," he said. "For the moment, it's Grimm's."

I laughed. "You're supposed to be a tough guy," I said. "Aren't you that guy who wrote the story where Sonny gets shot in the tollbooth?"

"Oh no," he said. "That's not the man I am, that's the man I'd like to be."

Chapter 11

The following year, when I wasn't working as a nurse, I spent most of my time at home on the manuscript for my book and Mario began to work on a book about the Sicilian bandit, Salvatore Guiliano.

Aside from my Thursday night meetings with my nursing friends, I'd run over to visit Mario a couple of times a week to talk "writing" and to just hang out.

He was upstairs in his study, always sitting at his desk.

More often than not, I'd run up the stairs, flop down on a chair across from him, and we'd start to talk about Erika. How he missed her, how different life was without her, how he hated that his kids had to take care of him now. "I always thought she'd be here for me when I was dying. I never expected her to die first. I was supposed to be the hero and when it really mattered, I couldn't do anything."

"That's hard," I said. "I mean I guess that's the hope and the bonus in a long marriage," I said. "Does that frighten you? The thought of being alone when you die?"

"Yes," he said. There was a long silence. "I failed her," he said. "I should have been able to do something."

"Even mythic heroes can't stop death," I said. "Not possible. That's Destiny's call." We spent hours discussing Erika to keep her memory alive. I knew he was comfortable talking with me about her because as he always put it, "we were combat buddies" while Erika was sick. On that night, to reassure him, I offered, "I know it's not the same. But if it helps at all, and if there is any way I'm able, I'll be with you when you're dying. I'll keep you company."

He smiled then, and patted my hand. "Life is full of surprises," he said. "You could be married to a rich oil man by then."

I laughed. "Usually I'm good with promises," I told him. "If there's any way I can be, I will be with you. I promise."

Then we'd both talk about books for a while. Often, I'd spill my worries over my patients, my craziness over the kids, and my uncertainty about ever being able to write well. I poured out everything I was afraid of, and passionately explained what I was furious about. I told him all the things I was afraid I couldn't do, how I couldn't capture what I wanted to on paper, how it was all too much and yet now, I wanted to do nothing more than write.

Mario looked up and said seriously, "You ever go to a quilting class?"

I laughed. "Me? Do I look like the kind of girl who quilts?"

He just smiled and I could see all that was going on behind his eyes. "Too bad," he said. "because writing is like that. You just start with one little patch. Then you put in as many details as you can."

"Patch?" I asked, puzzled.

"You want to write," he said. "Right?"

"Of course," I said. "I've met so many real-life heroes. I've seen so many miracles. I know how much medicine can do, and what it can't. I want to share those stories. About my patients, my heroes, all those people I took care of, all those people I loved."

He just nodded slowly. "Patches, patients, heroes, miracles. That's where you start. Just start telling those stories like you tell them to me," he said. "After all those patches are done, you'll see the patterns, then you can put them where they belong."

"You make it sound so easy," I said. "I know it can't be that easy."

"Simple, not easy," he said. "Different things. Just start. You only learn to write by writing—and rewriting. All writing is rewriting."

"There's got to be more to writing than that," I said.

"Use your own voice, that's the trick," he said. "Don't start writing like a college professor, that will kill you. Keep that voice, and you'll do fine."

Often, Mario wrote with a felt magic marker on yellow legal pads but his writing was unintelligible. Still, over those months I began to transcribe those pages, first on a typewriter than on a word processor.

It was during that time, I began see the beginnings of a pattern to my own life. Like how everything I did before prepared me for the steps that were coming up in my future. If I hadn't spent years trying to decipher doctors' scribble in order to save lives, I would never have been able to help Mario. Now I was an ace!

Once Mario sat with his pad or even at his typewriter, he was possessed, nothing broke his concentration. He heard nothing and said nothing.

His kids manned the phones, kept people from the front door, and took care of everything else so he could write.

When he was finished with his writing, he was completely present. Then he could listen for hours, as though he was totally interested even in the smallest things.

"How do you do that?" I asked him. "I mean listen as though it matters."

He smiled. "People interest me. I like stories. I'm always listening for a line one of my characters can use."

"But I've watched you listen to people, I mean waitresses, waiters, people who deliver your mail. You look as interested as when you listen to your writer friends. That's what I mean."

Mario had a look, a deep thoughtful and compassionate look when he listened. He explained, "Most people are fighting desperate battles that no one else can imagine. I just know that everyone is doing the best they can."

"But then how do you not get angry at all the injustices? How do you not fight harder for all the things you believe in?" I asked.

"People only do what they want to do," he said. "You can't change anyone. You can't rush evolution."

"Mario, I need some rules for writing," I told him one day as we were sitting at the kitchen table having rolls and coffee.

"What kind of rules?" he asked.

"Rules that will make the books I write best sellers," I said, laughing. "What else could I want?"

"Okay, that's easy," he said. "For a commercial book, just read the best seller lists. If the first three books on all the lists are about Lincoln, dogs, and apple pie, just write a book where Lincoln is sitting in front of a fireplace with his dog, eating apple pie."

I made a face. "I'm serious," I said.

"So am I," he said. "If you want to be a writer, write what you know and what you believe in. If you want to write a bestseller, you've got to know what touches a nerve in your readers. Two different things."

"Okay," I said. "Just tell me how to write a book that I believe in that people will want to read."

"Forget the rules," he said, reaching over to pick up the Sunday paper that one of his sons had brought earlier and placed on the table. "Just write a good book and tell a good story. Then in order to be a better writer, write more. After that rewrite, and rewrite again."

"What does that mean?" I asked.

"Writing is rewriting," he said.

"Okay, go on," I said. "That's rule #1."

"What?" he said, absently as he picked up the Times and held it in front of his face. He read everything, all the time.

I reached across the table and pushed the paper down. "Come on, Mario," I pleaded, "just give me 10 minutes of undivided attention, ten minutes of talking to me, and then I'll shut up for the rest of the day and you can read and write to your heart's content."

He squinted as he looked at me. "What do you want me to say?" he asked.

"I want to ask some questions about writing," I said.

"Okay, he said. "Fire away, what do you want to know?" He lowered his glasses and looked at me. "I give you my undivided attention," he teased.

"Thank you," I said. "Aside from writing is rewriting, what's another rule?"

He looked serious when he said. "Names are important. Not only how they sound, but how they look on the page. The names of your characters should be different enough from each other that the reader doesn't get mixed up."

I was writing notes on one of the napkins. Mario looked amused.

"Go on," I said.

"Let me think," he said, taking a sip of decaf. "A writer should always have some affection for his or her characters. You don't have to like them, but you have to understand them. You have to be able to feel some sympathy even for the worst of them."

"Why would that be?" I asked.

"Because if you aren't interested, why should the reader be? The reader has to have someone to root for. If you haven't made the character complex enough that you understand how he feels, then the character is not fully drawn enough and he or she becomes a caricature," Mario said.

"I don't know if I agree with you," I said to him. "If one of my characters does something despicable, something that I find morally objectionable, why do I have to feel sympathy for him? Or her for that matter?"

Mario tilted his head to the side and studied me for a few minutes. "A story becomes interesting when characters play against each other because they see a situation or experience their world in different ways. That difference in perception and the action that follows is what causes the tension in a story."

"Tension?" I repeated.

"A story needs an engine," he explained. "Something or someone that moves the story forward. Something that keeps the reader turning the pages."

"I'm not sure I get that," I said. "I mean I understand the concept, but I don't really get the picture."

"Remember to start your chapters with a hook. Something you plant and leave unfinished. Something the reader wants to discover badly enough that it keeps them reading. Don't rush your story. The reader will wait. They'll give you time."

"I hope you're right," I said.

"Start with a good beginning, give your story a strong engine, finish with a good payoff and your readers will forgive you for what you do in the middle."

"They will?" I said. "What keeps the reader reading in the middle?"

"The hooks, the engine—and the affection for the characters that you've made them care about. Those characters have to grow and change, and the reader should be invested enough in them to want to know what happens."

"What else?" I said.

Mario laughed and said. "Your ten minutes is up."

Without another word, he lifted his paper in front of his face and began to read again.

"Hey," I hollered, "Is that all? Just tell me."

"Be patient," Mario said, picking up a hard roll and taking a bite, and his eyes lit up. "There's more, of course."

"Then why did you stop?" I asked.

"That's a hook," he said.

Chapter 12

I saw Mario on Wednesday nights and sometimes I'd run over for the weekend when he was at home, to discuss a problem I was having and to talk about how everyone in the family was doing.

We'd go out to eat, and then when we got home, we'd watch some movies. We'd talk about plot structure and casting.

When we went out to dinner for the first time at a local Italian restaurant in town called, "La Trestavera," the waiters wore black suits and bow ties, and draped white napkins over their arms. But their attitude was so casual, I totally enjoyed it. Everyone greeted Mario and spoke to him in Italian.

He smiled and nodded but didn't speak.

They showed us to a small round table in the corner of the room covered with a crisp white tablecloth and napkins.

"Once we sat down at the table, I asked Mario, "What was that waiter saying to you?"

"Don't know," he said.

I frowned. "What do you mean?" I asked.

"I don't speak Italian," he said.

I started to laugh. "Really?" I said. "I thought I was the only Italian who didn't."

When the waiter brought the menus, both of us looked over it but I was stumped. "I know some of these dishes," I said. "My mom cooks them, but don't have a clue about most."

"So let's get a couple of dishes, and just taste them," he said. "That way we'll know for sure."

When the waiter came, I let Mario order for both of us. But as I listened I almost fell over dead. "Mario," I whispered, "Isn't that too much?"

He ordered five dishes for himself and two for me.

"I can't eat that much food," I said.

"I know," he said. "Eat what you want."

When the food came, I watched as Mario tried one dish after another, without looking up once. "Good," he said. "The food is good here."

I sat frozen.

Finally, he looked up at me and said, "Why do you look as though you've just seen a train wreck?"

"Because you have diabetes and I'm afraid you're going to keel over dead and I'm going to have to do something about it," is all I said.

But what I was also thinking was that my father, who lived by the motto "everything in moderation", would have been horrified.

"Hey, Mario," I asked that night. "If we wind up going out, if we wind up in a real relationship, you know my kids have to come first. I mean your kids have to come first for you, but any messing with my kids is a deal breaker."

Mario smiled. "No question. You've got your dynasty, I've got mine. I'll be the King of England, and you can be the King of France."

"King?" I said, "Why not Queen of France."

"My dear," Mario said, seriously. "You must know that all the Queens were beheaded!"

So we agreed. That was how it would always be.

Later that month, Mario and I were working on research for his book about the Sicilian bandit, Salvatore Guiliano, which would later be called "The Sicilian." By eight p.m. it was time to take a break. "I'm not getting the feel I need for this book," he said. "History is constraining me."

"What does that mean?" I asked.

Mario said, "Facts limit my power of invention. I just can't seem to see it clearly enough."

"Doesn't that sometimes happen to writers?" I asked. "The fear of the blank page?"

"Yes," he said. "But this is different."

"We could try to tape it," I suggested. "I mean you could tell me the whole Robin Hood story as you have before, and later I could transcribe it and you could correct it."

Mario frowned. "Can't work like that," he said. "Writing is different from talking."

"Could we just give it a try?" I said. "Just so you don't have to face a blank page?"

"You're on the wrong track," he said. "When I write the story comes alive. When I talk about it, something gets lost."

But I haunted, and he tried. Several times. The story was flat and the words wouldn't come. After a couple of weeks, and several trashed tapes, Mario and I were again in the study...and he was pacing, frustrated.

"There's only one solution," he said. "We have to go to Sicily. I have to walk where Guiliano walked. I have to see the caves in the mountains where he hid. I have to visit the cemetery where he and his best friend, Piciotti, are buried."

"When?" I asked.

"Soon," he said. "I can't think of anything else."

"Well, can't we just try taping one more time?" I asked. "Just to humor me?"

"Sure," he said. "But then we go to Sicily."

That night, I cooked us dinner, my favorite of steak, potato, and salad.

It might have been the 20th time we sat down over dinner to try to discuss the dynamics of our relationship. Mario liked the unspoken, it saved him from commitment. I liked to know what to expect. Still, he never believed in sharing too much information. Information was power and secretly, he believed that someday a woman would betray him. Secretly? Not so secret because he kept telling me. But I was determined not to fall into his trap.

"I can't be responsible for what you believe other women did to you," I said, "All I can tell you is that I would never betray you. I could never betray you."

"It's in all the literature, my dear," he said.

"Okay, then, what kind of a relationship do you think we should have?" I asked him.

"A good one," he said. "A productive one. We should write books together. Each our own of course. I don't collaborate. Until after I'm dead."

I made a face. "Mario, why would you think I wanted to write the kinds of books you do? I want to write books that heal. Books that give hope. Books that can help change the world."

Mario put more butter on his baked potato. "Big job," he said.

I shook my head. "Don't get off topic," I said, laughing. "I meant do you want to have a mad love affair, or do you want to have a deep and intimate friendship?"

He looked up at me and rolled his eyes. He sounded very amused when he said, "We could never have a great love affair. Each of us is too selfish, too committed to our own work."

"You've said that before but then what is this for you? One of those cliché Pygmalion relationships where you mold me into whatever you want?"

He started to laugh so hard, he almost choked. "You credit me with more courage than I have, my dear," he said. "Me, mold you? A frightening prospect."

"Well, if we became real lovers, besides being writing buddies, what I'm asking is, do you want a monogamous relationship?"

"Monogamous?" he said as though he didn't understand.

I laughed. "You know, the kind where we promise to be faithful forever?"

He looked up and smiled at me. His eyes glittered with amusement. "No one can promise to be faithful forever," he explained. "Life changes things. Each day when you get out of bed, danger lurks around every corner. Temptations spring up like mushrooms. Life is full of surprises."

"Well, I can promise to be faithful forever," I said without hesitation.

"Then you lack imagination," he said.

"What are you saying?" I asked, impassioned now. "When I fall madly in love, I can be faithful forever."

He looked doubtful. "No one can promise that," he repeated.

"I can," I said with certainty.

"Honey," he said, and he tried to say it gently so it didn't sound like a reproach. "You've already left two husbands. I'm not accusing you of anything, I'm just saying, anything can happen."

"Well, of course," I said. "I know life is full of surprises. That's not what I'm talking about. What I meant is the I could be faithful forever, *unless something happens.*"

Mario threw his head back and laughed. He laughed so hard that tears ran down his cheeks. "Oh," he said. "*That* kind of faithful! I can promise that. I can be faithful forever too unless something happens."

That was our deal, in so many things, it was the bedrock of our relationship—and it brought us both to laughter and to freedom.

Chapter 13

Nothing can protect you from Life's plan. Neither organic vegetables or virtue can protect you. Education and money can't protect you, though being smart can help and being rich can help pretend a better battle. Who you know and what you do makes no difference. The Source of our existence is an equal opportunity employer. You're on earth, doing time, anything goes.

So, once I got the hang of being a nurse and the understanding that it meant anyone of the people I was taking care of could be me, I was a lot more patient, a lot more careful, and a lot kinder. Also, a lot more afraid, unless I was in the hospital, or taking care of other people, not while I was out in the regular world doing what regular people did...and I must also say, seemed to enjoy!

Thank God, Mario didn't like to drink or dance or I would have been sunk. After so many years of being on the singles scene between marriages, after dating—and not dating—in order to keep the fear of dying at bay, I was tired of party sounds and dance music. I was exhausted by acting as though I enjoyed it, just to feel a part of what made others feel alive. Mario was a godsend for me. A man who liked to lay around reading, discussing great ideas and telling stories. I could do that. I liked that. Sitting home or in his study was safe for me. I could just be me, and enjoy it.

Unfortunately, the man did want to go out into the world now and then. He did love to meet with his friends, eat at restaurants, and gamble. He needed to get away from his characters and whatever book he was writing so that he could breathe in a world other than the one he was creating.

Mostly we went out to eat at Elaine's in NY, or The Palm or Pearl's in LA. Back at home on Long Island, we went to the same Italian restaurant almost every week. They knew him, and he loved their food so after a while, it just seemed like being with another family.

Elaine's on the other hand was very different for me. Mario loved the owner, Elaine, and loved the restaurant. He always re-membered how even when he was a struggling writer, Elaine would let him run up a tab until he had enough money to pay it. From the day he became famous, he felt he owed her as much loyalty and respect as she had offered him. Mario never forgot a kindness, he was like that.

Elaine's, the favorite hangout of writers and actors in the city.

Usually Mario met with all his good buddies once a week and they'd always go into Chinatown, Elaine's, or the Palm in New York City. Joe Heller, Mel Brooks, Bruce J Friedman, Speed Vogel, and Joe Stein, when he was in town, and the man Mario thought was the smartest guy he ever met, an artist, writer and one of his very best friends, George Mandel.

Elaine, the owner, was brash and outspoken, and didn't much care whose feelings she hurt, but she was always kind to me. After a while, I got comfortable with her but not with seeing all those famous peo-ple. Partly because it played with my perceptions.

Imagine a room filled with people whose faces you recognize, and yet you can't remember where you know them from. Can't remember even enough to make small talk. It was though I walked onto a movie set without a script.

We'd walk through the door into a dark and very crowded room and the waiters would greet us with a warm hello, then Elaine would hug us and walk us through the restaurant to a favorite table in the back. Often, we'd pass Woody Allen and Mia Farrow, some-times Shirley MacLaine, lots of writers I didn't know, and some that Mario did, and some movie actors who were appearing on Broadway.

Unlike the "at the ready" feeling of confidence and competence I had in a hospital when there was an emergency and I knew who to call or what to do, in a room so crowded with familiar, unfamiliar faces, I was completely disoriented. People would approach and greet us, and Mario would always nod and smile, saying not one word that could give me a clue to who they were. So, I'd nod too, and try to smile, but suddenly I'd be in the middle of a full-blown panic attack. Often, we barely made it to our table before I needed to escape into the bathroom to hide.

One of the very first times it happened, I was making a bee line to the restroom, and bumped into a very tall, really good looking young man. He had a dazzling smile and seemed genuinely surprised when I mumbled some apology.

"Where are you going in such a rush?" he asked and laughed.

I knew him. I mean I thought I knew him. He was so familiar, I should have known his name. Did I? No. Not one coherent thought or clue to his identity.

"Restroom," was all I said.

He pointed to the back corner of the room. "Are you okay? Do you want me to walk you there?" he asked, with complete sincerity.

He didn't seem like a stranger, so I just said, "Sure. You're tall enough to get us through this crowd."

He smiled and walked me back to the restroom.

In the bathroom I stood against the wall for a long time just trying to take some deep breaths and relax. Then I threw some water on my face. After several minutes, I whipped up my courage, and walked back out into the crowd to make my way to our table where Mario was waiting patiently.

When I looked over my shoulder, as I sat down, I saw the young man and he waved. Mario nodded.

"Who is he?" I asked Mario. "Do we know him? I mean have we met him before? I just ran into him."

Mario laughed. "Yes," Mario said. "We know him."

"I can't remember," I said. "Who is he?"

"Did you ever see Superman?" he asked me.

"Don't be funny," I said. "You wrote Superman."

"Yes," he said. "He's Superman."

"Oh crap! Christopher Reeve," I whispered. "It's him. It *is* him."

"Yes, my dear," Mario said.

"Well, what the heck is he doing in New York?" I asked. "If I bumped into him in LA, or if he was on a stretcher in a hospital I would have recognized him," I said. "But in NY? In Elaine's? You make me crazy."

"What are we going to eat?" Mario asked.

"I can't get my bearings," I told him. "Order whatever."

"Okay," he said. Then all he did was signal Elaine and before we knew it the table was filled with different dishes, all great looking and pretty much delicious. But all I could do as I ate my steak and smothered my baked potato with pounds of butter was say. "I mean who doesn't know Christopher Reeve?" Even I, who had spent years locked in hospitals, living on the side roads of the main highways of life, should have recognized him. Christopher Reeve.

But it wasn't until much later, in terms I understood, after he had fallen off his horse, gotten paralyzed, and fought a really courageous battle with life, did I really know him. Christopher Reeve. He *was* Superman.

Chapter 14

There was no getting around it, in order to get a handle on The Sicilian, Mario insisted we fly to Montelepre, Guiliano's birthplace. Because his Italian publisher wanted to meet him, Mario and I flew to Rome first before we could continue on to Sicily.

At the airport, we were met by his Italian publisher, Paolo. From there we would fly to Palermo, then drive to Montelepre so we could visit the birthplace of the famous Robin Hood bandit, Salvatore Guiliano.

Paolo was warm and welcoming and so excited to meet Mario that he took us on a whirlwind tour of the city.

First we visited the Vatican and stood in the square watching several people prepare the balcony on which the Pope stood as he blessed the devout each Sunday morning. There, Paolo insisted I take pictures of him with Mario that he could show to the editors back at the publishing house.

After we had a delicious lunch of the best spaghetti I had ever tasted, and had more pictures taken, Paolo drove us to the Coliseum, the Forum, he walked us around the ancient ruins and then took us to the famous Hassler hotel to check in because he knew what few people did, that neither Mario or I could speak Italian.

Mario reassured him that we would be fine and thanked him for all he had done, essentially telling him it was time to go.

Once we were outside again, Paolo explained that afternoon we would fly to Palermo, where we would be met by our special guide and escort, Joseph, who would drive us to the best hotel in Palermo, Grand Hotel Villa Igiea. Once we were settled, Joseph would drive us anywhere we wanted to go.

Then Paolo gave Mario his best wishes for a profitable trip but he warned, "If you find trouble in Palermo, we are ready to help. The Embassy here has informed those who must know and they have been alerted to your coming."

"Is there a problem?" Mario asked.

Paolo waved his hand in a dismissive gesture. "It is only a rumor, Signor Puzo." Then he leaned over and whispered something in Mario's ear.

"What's up?" I asked Mario.

Mario just shook his head and shrugged. "Something about the Guiliano family not wanting me to come near Montelepre."

"So what are we going to do?" I asked.

"Pay no attention, my dear," he said. "It is Sicily after all."

As Mario and I walked across the Tarmac to the small terminal in Palermo, I was overwhelmed by the magnificence of the mountains which seemed to spring from the sea and cut into the cloudless blue sky. I have never before or since seen a color that was as alive as the azure blue sky in Sicily on that day.

As Paolo had said, our guide was already waiting to greet us. Joseph was a tall pleasant young man, with dark curly hair and a beard. He was dressed in a dark suit and tie, and spoke English well enough for us to understand everything he said. He led us into the dark blue Mercedes car that had been provided for us by the publisher and just as we were about to pull away from the curb, several dark cars pulled up alongside us. Joseph got out to speak to them.

When he returned he turned to us and said, "Those who are entrusted with your safety are waiting to welcome you."

Before we knew it we were being escorted by the two cars, one on each side, as we went speeding along the streets of Palermo.

"What's going on?" I asked Mario.

"Patience, my dear," he said. "I have no doubt that we will find out shortly."

"Is there anything I should or shouldn't say?" I asked him.

He smiled. "Under these circumstances, I must caution you to say as little as possible."

"Hmmmm...." was all I said.

We arrived at what Joseph explained was the American Embassy in Rome, a very formidable building with several large pillars and a very long set of marble steps. Upstairs, we met several people who seemed only to want to shake Mario's hand. Finally, one man said, "The Guiliano family seems upset that you will come to their town. We wish to offer our assistance for your protection."

"Thank you for your gracious offer," Mario said softly. "I will certainly take you up on it, if we feel the need."

Once back in the car, Joseph asked, "To the Hotel, Signor Puzo?"

Without any hesitation, Mario said, "To Montelepre, Joseph."

"But Mario," I said, "I thought those guys just warned you there was danger in Montelepre."

Mario pulled out one of his big long black cigars and said, "We'll be in and out before they know it!"

"You're not worried?" I asked.

Mario just looked at me and said, "We are here to do research, my dear. What harm can there be?"

"I don't know," I said. "But if there is nothing to worry about, why are they worried?"

"It's a mystery," was all he said.

The ride to Montelepre from Palermo was treacherous for me. Between my nerves and the roller coaster roads, my stomach threatened me the whole ride there. I tried to close my eyes, but I couldn't really rest and I was starting to get a headache. Alongside the narrow road, the sparse terrain looked ominous. Several rocky cave-like structures, dotted the arid landscape. Mario pointed up to one of the mountaintops. "That's where he hid for all those years, Joseph?" he asked.

"That's what they say," Joseph said.

"He and his band, including Piscciotti?" Mario asked.

"Always in the hills and mountains," Joseph said. "Until he came to see his family now and then."

"Who?" I asked.

"Guiliano," Mario said. "The Robin Hood bandit."

"Was he a good guy or a bad guy for real?" I asked.

"Depends on your point of view," he said. "Some thought he was a terrorist, some thought a savior."

Just then we were passing a cemetery filled with terra cotta colored mausoleums. "Stop Joseph!" Mario said.

Joseph pulled into the driveway. He got out of the car and walked up to the tall decorative black wrought iron gate.

"It is locked I'm afraid," he said, returning to the car.

Mario opened his door. "Come out," he said to me.

There was a tall stucco wall surrounding the cemetery for as far as we could see. On the arch above the gate, there was a metal legend.

"What does that say? I asked Joseph.

"We were once as you are. You will be as we are."

"Pretty catchy," I said. "I mean Italians sure do get right to the point."

Mario's eyes were scanning the grounds. "We need some pictures," he said. Joseph and I looked at him. "Of what?" I asked.

"Guiliano's mausoleum and Piciotti's," he said. "They were best friends. They're both here. That's the story."

"Want me to climb over and unlock the gate?" I asked. "Maybe I can find the gatekeeper."

They both looked at me.

"If Joseph and you hold your hands together, I can get over, get in and take some pictures," I offered.

"You'll get arrested and hauled away to jail," Mario said.

"Then we'll have more research," I said. "Really, what can they do?"

Joseph tried to warn us...but then, Mario said, "We have a book to write, my dear. Think of this as a sacrifice to art."

So Joseph and Mario put their hands together and I climbed onto the ledge of the wall. As I was looking down to find a soft place to land when I jumped, I heard a voice call to me. But it was in Italian, so...

Suddenly, an old man with a peaked bill hat appeared at the gate. He was dressed in baggy woolen pants and a heavy cotton shirt.

Mario and Joseph talked to him. I saw Mario reach into his pocket and pull out some bills, and hand it to the man. Suddenly, the gate opened.

Then Mario looked up and over toward me. "My dear," he said, "You must come down."

By the time Joseph got me off the wall, and ran to get the camera, Mario had disappeared between the buildings and the tall palm trees. Joseph walked beside me, handed me the camera, and waited while I called for Mario. Again and again. No answer.

Finally, just as I was about to give up and go back to the car, I heard Mario call.

"Take some pictures?" he asked, pointing to one mausoleum and then to another.

And so I did. It's hard to describe the peace I felt in that cemetery, surrounded by the sacred silence of all those who had walked through life before me. But instead of being creepy, it was somehow reassuring as I walked between the aisles taking pictures and reading names on the old metal plates. I said a prayer before I left, and felt a strange longing. I wanted to know who they were, how they'd lived, and who they'd loved.

But back in the car was another story. That road was treacherous and finally when Joseph announced, "We are only moments from the town, Signor."

Mario said, "Pull over, Joseph. I want to speak to you."

Joseph stopped the car and turned around to look at Mario.

"Joseph," Mario said, "We will ride into Montelepre and you will take us through the town for a quick look around. Then you will park, and we will get out and walk around. Stay back and let me walk ahead. We will meet at the car when we are ready to leave."

"What happens to me?" I asked Mario.

"You stay back with Joseph," he said. "Walk around like a tourist, taking pictures. Don't call to me, or talk to me. Act as though we don't know each other."

Joseph put the car in gear and started to drive again. Within minutes, he made a sharp right into what looked like a sunken driveway right into the small town. He rode down one narrow street after another—went into one alley after another until suddenly we were in the center of town.

"Joseph, here," Mario said, opening the door. "Park the car, then follow me, but not too close."

Mario got out and I went with Joseph to park. I took my camera and hung it around my neck. As I looked up at the tall thin stucco houses, behind shuttered windows, I could see the wooden slats on the shutters raise and dark eyes peeking out. The streets were almost empty except for an occasional old man in a peaked cap, walking alone, head down.

I walked through the town with Joseph, behind Mario, watching as Mario pulled out one of his long black El Presidente cigars. He stopped and lit it with deliberation, tossed the match on the sidewalk and continued to walk through the center of town. I just kept snapping pictures.

Finally, we came upon several old men sitting on a wooden bench under a tree. Several others were playing bocci. To the right of the game there was a beautiful Catholic church, a choir singing from inside.

Mario walked past the church, and nodded to the men. They looked up but quickly looked down again, and I could hear them mumble. As he turned to cross the street, several of the men looked up again, but only for a moment, then lowered their heads quickly.

Mario nodded. A slow exaggerated nod of recognition, and the men all bowed their heads again.

Mario turned toward the church. Stood fixed for a moment. I didn't see the big man in the dark suit standing on the steps next to the priest until later. But Mario had seen him. His cigar was a big as Mario's.

I turned to say something to Joseph, when I saw one of the men make the sign of the cross as Mario walked away.

I turned to Joseph, but he grabbed my arm and turned me around to walk back to the car. Suddenly Mario was right behind us.

"Joseph, quickly," he said. "Time to go."

But that was easier said than done.

Once we all piled into the car, Joseph went down one narrow street after another, hitting a dead end. Time after time, street after street, there seemed no way out. The shutters on the windows above us all seemed to open at once.

"There's the Guiliano house," Joseph said, pointing to one small house with a colorful Coat of Arms in front.

Mario said, "Stop," and before I could reach for him, he was out of the car.

"Take a picture," he said. And I did.

Mario jumped back in the car and said, "No time to dally, my sweet." Then, "Joseph, take us back to Palermo. Now."

The Hotel Igiea was a beautiful hotel in the city of Palermo right on the sea. The terracotta tiles covered the long halls and the lavish suite we had was magnificent. The restaurant cooked the best meals we had in Sicily, and the staff was friendly and courteous. The only problem was that we were cautioned not to leave the hotel after 8 at night. A curfew.

Mario had several interviews to do while he was in Palermo, and he didn't want me with him. I sulked and then finally said, "I hate this. Why do I have to go shopping or get lost with Joseph, while you're doing all these interviews? I want to see how it goes, I want to learn too. After all, if I'm a writer too, why can't I come?"

Finally, after haunting him several times, one night as we were lying in bed, just before we went to sleep, I accused him of being embarrassed to be with me. "You just don't want anyone to know about us."

He just looked at me and frowned. "You make me want to kill you when you talk like that," he said. "But that would be a crime of passion, and I'm a reasonable man."

"Well then, give me a reasonable explanation," I said. "And I won't mention it again."

He got out of bed and reached for a cigar. He lit it and sat back down on the bed. Then he turned to me. "It is just a matter of practicality," he explained. "I don't want to get a shoebox with your ear in it. Then I'll have to pay a ransom, and it will cost my kids their inheritance. It is a simple and reasonable precaution."

I laughed. "Mario, you read too many Mafia books. Your imagination is just running wild. But I did promise, so I'll shop with Joseph while you do the 'celebrity' thing. Still, I think this is crazy."

Two days later, the day we left Palermo, only hours after we boarded the plane to return to Rome, there was a great slaughter in the streets of Palermo. It was the beginning of the Second Mafia war.

When we heard about it we were already in Rome. I apologized for doubting Mario's sense of danger and his desire to protect me. He gave me a pair of gold cameo earrings to thank me for coming to Sicily with him.

I was grateful I still had two ears to hang them on.

Chapter 15

Rome is a beautiful city but in sharp contrast to all the elegant shops beneath the Spanish Steps, I was surprised to see several Carabinieri or uniformed police, armed with rifles, in the street and outside the hotel—no lofty manners as in London.

Mario checked in at the front desk at the Hassler Hotel but instead of walking upstairs with me to check out the suite, he sat in one of the tapestry loveseats in the front lobby and began to read the paperback book he was carrying. The Concierge came up to him and asked, "Signor Puzo? Are you ready for your suite?"

But Mario waved toward me and said, "Show the suite to Madame. If she likes it, we'll call the bellman to bring our luggage up."

I excused myself and the concierge stood a respectful distance away while I sat down next to Mario to talk to him. "What's going on?" I asked him. "Why am I going upstairs alone?"

"Because if you like it, I'll like it," he said. "If you don't, it won't matter if I like it."

"That's not completely true," I said, frowning "I've stayed in places with you that I haven't liked and I didn't torture you for it."

"That's true," he said. "But there were times when you didn't like a suite and we changed it, isn't that also true?"

"Yes, but then it was because you agreed you liked the one I chose better," I defended.

"That's true," he said. "So why would I go upstairs, bring the luggage, begin to unpack and if you didn't like it, change suites when I'll get the best one if I just sit here and read?"

"Because this feels funny," I said. "I like to include you in my decisions."

He raised his eyebrows but said nothing.

"You're really going to make me do this thing alone?" I asked.

He lowered his book and told the concierge, "If Madame likes the suite, call the front desk and let me know. I'll be right up."

"I'll like it," I told him. "I promise I'll like it."

"Then I'll see you upstairs," Mario said, smiling good-naturedly. When he picked up his book to read again, I knew the conversation was over.

The upstairs hallway of the third floor was wallpapered in colorful wildflowers on a warm yellow background which was light and pretty. As I followed the concierge, I felt confident. Even as he put his key in the door, I was wondering how long it would take Mario to get a bellman to carry our bags up to the room.

Finally, with great showmanship, the concierge threw open the door to the suite, and announced, "One of our very finest suites, Signora."

I stood looking at it stunned, frozen in place. The walls were covered in dark blue taffeta, the drapes were dark blue velvet, and the bedspread was dark blue satin with cream lace trim. The living room walls and furniture matched. Mario hated dark colors.

"Very rich looking," I said but there was no heart in it.

The concierge frowned.

"I have to go downstairs and speak with Mr. Puzo," I told him.

I raced ahead of the concierge to reach the elevator first.

"Is there some trouble Signora?" he asked me more than once in the elevator, but I was speechless.

Mario was sitting in the same position in the front lobby and I ran over to him. "You're right," I said. "I hate it. It looks like the Addams Family lives there."

"I told you, you wouldn't like it," he said.

"Why?" I asked, "Have you seen it before? I thought you'd never been here."

"Law of averages," he said. "You can't like everything."

"You're teasing me because I complained in Washington that one time and that other time in Vegas, right?" I asked. "But didn't I get us better suites both times because I was willing to be the bad guy? Admit you hated them too."

"Absolutely," he said. "That's why I suggested this. It's a great solution. So what did the concierge say?"

"I didn't tell him," I said. "You tell him. He's an Italian. They listen to men better than women."

"Remind me to tell you a story about that later..." Mario said.

The concierge asked, "Would Signor like to see our famous suite?"

"Certainly," he said.

So now both of us got into the elevator, followed the concierge upstairs, walked down the long colorful corridor, and waited while the concierge opened the door again.

Mario stepped in before me, and the concierge folded his arms and waited patiently by the open door. Then I walked behind Mario as he walked through each room and looked around. "Ahh..." was all he said, again and again. Loud enough for the concierge to hear.

"Ahh...what?" I finally whispered.

"Ahh, you're right, I hate it," he whispered back.

"Okay, so you're going to tell him to get us another suite, right?" I asked.

"Of course, my dear," he said. "Would you doubt me?"

I was so relieved that I finally exhaled.

But when Mario walked up to the concierge, he held both palms upward in a helpless gesture and said, "Signor, but what can I do? It is a beautiful suite, but the Signora doesn't like it. You understand." He followed it with a long pregnant pause.

But now that he'd heard the verdict, the concierge scowled and put his hands on his hips. "Signore, this is the finest hotel in Roma. And this is the one of our finest suites. I apologize, but we can do no better."

"Can we have worse?" I asked.

"My dear...." Mario cautioned.

"Each of our suites and all of our rooms are inhabited," he said. "There is not one empty place."

"Then we must accept your hospitality and be grateful," Mario said, smiling at him. He put his arm around my shoulder. "I'm certain when Signora looks again she will appreciate its charm."

"Grazia Signore," the concierge said as Mario tipped him generously. "The bellman will be up with your luggage in a moment."

Now I was mad. "How could you to that to me?" I asked. "How could you set me up like that and then not back me up?"

"My dear," he said, sounding terribly sincere, "In the face of this obstacle, I made the only reasonable decision. Either accept this fine suite or waste hours looking for another hotel."

"The fact that you sold me down the river and made me look foolish doesn't trouble you at all?"

"Of course it does, my dear," he said, "But the guidebooks give the restaurant in this hotel the highest rating. The only problem is that they say reservations must be made months in advance. Under these circumstances, I'm certain the concierge wants to make you happy and so when I ask for a reservation for tonight, he will try his best to grant our wish."

"Your wish," I said. "For me I'm left only with the knowledge that you betrayed me for a dish of macaroni."

"But the finest, my dear," he said smiling.

"Stop calling me my dear," I said. "It's condescending."

Mario walked around the suite again, then he sat in one of the dark living room chairs. "I hate dark colors," he said. "They depress me."

"Don't even go there," I warned.

"Why?" he said. "I'm admitting you're right. I hate this suite. I'm agreeing with you, I thought you'd be pleased."

Then he patted the seat alongside him and I sat down. Within minutes, I was almost over it and I said, "Hey, if any vampires come creeping around here tonight, I'm sending them right over to your side of the bed."

Mario looked at me horrified. "Now how am I supposed to sleep?"

"Maybe you'll eat so much of that delicious spaghetti, that it will put you into a coma and you'll never know."

"You're a mean little thing," he said.

"I am," I agreed.

Chapter 16

No matter what Mario told me about writing, about how hard it was or how much work it would be, I still wasn't prepared. I was surprised at how much courage it took to put a story down on paper and look at the characters in black and white. Because I was writing about me, my family, and my friends in intimate nursing situations in different hospitals, I had to be even more careful.

Mario was so right when he said, "You can't lie on paper. Lies are too easy to spot. The audience will see through it. You can't trick the reader if you want him to suspend his disbelief. You have to do a real magic trick if you call it fiction, but even then, you have to tell a truth."

"I'm not sure I understand what you're saying," I said.

"You can't use sleight of hand," he said. "You can't take a reader, make him believe something, use that as a premise, then suddenly give your main character amnesia or take the easy way out. The character has to be true to himself. Even in the worst of them, the writer has to see something that helps him understand his character or the reader won't. If the writer doesn't, the reader can't. Even if one of the characters doesn't know something about another, the writer has to tip off the reader."

"What about the twists of plot?" I asked. "Doesn't that happen in books when you don't expect it."

"Yes, he said. "You can have the reader looking to the right, when you bring something in from the left, but you can't expect a reader to believe a mother can pick her kids up in her arms and fly to the grocery store. It has to make sense to that world. Unless it's science fiction and then that's a different world and a different skill."

I spent the following year doing private duty nursing, taking care of the kids, hanging out with my nurse friends, and in every spare moment, writing pieces of MY BOOK.

Each piece or quilt patch, as Mario called them, each small story, forced me back into the love and the pain of each of the patients I took care of. It reawakened all my memories and insisted I put them on paper, in words often too small to hold the emotions I was feeling. I cried, forced myself to keep writing even when I seemed ridiculous to myself, even when I wondered when in each piece I had done the right thing. I reexamined every one of my decisions and always asked myself, could I have done any of it better? On the page, could the reader feel what I felt?

Mario said, "Can't edit while writing. Create first, then go back and rewrite. You'll kill the story if you're trying to make sense of it while you're telling it."

"Well if I don't tell them what the character was feeling then how can they know?"

"Show it," he said. "Don't tell it. Use every sense you can, sight, smell, touch, and sound. Use details to nail them into the reality that your character lives in. If you write it well enough, they'll get it. If they don't get it, you haven't written it well enough."

I huffed and puffed and wanted to be so true to my characters that every piece of dialogue had to sound like I remembered, exactly. Then, there was the question of names.

Again, Mario said, "Be careful with the names. Names are important. Use some common sense in choosing names."

"Like what?" I asked.

"Don't call a hero doctor, Dr. Slaughter. No one thing will make or break a book, but lots of tiny little things can," he said. "Give the reader some credit. They'll give you time to tell your story."

It was overwhelming for me. I had taken only two writing courses and though I had spent my whole life reading books, there was still so much I had to learn.

At the time, I didn't even know the difference between a novel and a non-fiction book. I didn't understand the difference between an autobiography, a biography, a memoir, or a novel. For me, a book was a book. I was more nervous about writing a chapter of that book than I was about jumping on someone's chest to try to bring them back to life.

I made all the novice mistakes anyone could. I was overly sentimental, I was defensive, in an attempt not to make myself too wimpy, I made myself too harsh. I kept making excuses for the character that was me. I worried about how my friends would feel if I left them out, or if I painted them as I truly saw them. I just knew my mother and father would hate the way I depicted them. And who even knew if my kids would ever forgive me?

"That's why it takes courage to write," Mario said. "If you're going to tell the truth, some people will hate you. But if you don't tell the truth, there's no sense being a writer. You only write if you feel you've got something to say. You got to forget all that crap. You're either a writer or you're not."

So, I wrote, and then wrote some more. By the time I finished the original manuscript, it was 750 pages.

It was only because I was a nurse that I had to write. It was not only because I was too exhausted to keep fighting for one patient at a time. It was also because I saw no other way to acknowledge both the inhumanity in medicine and the divinity in humanity that I needed to write. I wanted to share both the horror and the miracles that I was witness to. Besides, I did want to stamp death and disease out of the Western Hemisphere. But was that enough?

It had been one of those weekends where Mario and I were working nonstop from morning till night, locked in his study, hanging his oaktag charts on the walls, organizing chapters, brainstorming, and typing pages.

His study was built high on stilts and so he called it his tree house. Our desks were on opposite sides of the room and our windows faced different trees. We'd sit back to back for long hours, each in our own headspace, often not a word passed between us. I usually waited for him to talk first because his thoughts were harder for him to speak and share.

That evening after I cooked dinner, and we were at the kitchen table eating, he looked pensive. "What's up?" I asked. "I thought we had a really good day."

"We did," he said. "A very good day. I'm a much nicer person when I can write than when I can't," he added.

"You're pretty nice most of the time," I told him. "You just don't talk a lot."

He began as though he was continuing. "I was wondering how long it will take women to catch on to the fact that marriage is a bad deal for them."

"Oh, no," I said. "We had such a good day, and I didn't even mention getting married."

"I know, I know," he said. "I was just wondering about it myself. Wondering about how long it would be before men became extinct."

"You're kidding me, right?" I asked.

"Not at all," he said, shaking his head. "I mean look at what women can do now."

"What does that mean?" I asked. "What could they not do before?"

"Well, before they needed men to protect them, to hunt and bring food, to support them," he said. "But now especially with computers and alarm systems, why would they need men?"

"Some women like men," I said laughing. "I like men." I didn't tease him about boy toys because he seemed so serious.

"Men don't understand women," he said. "I didn't understand women until you explained them to me. Now, I understand."

"Mario," I said. "I think more like a man than a woman. That's why you understand me. I lay it all out there and I don't play games. I don't try to trick men, because there's no percentage in it for me. If I manipulate a man and he falls for it, I lose respect for him. If I lose respect for him, I lose too. It's simple."

"Honey, get me some Coke," he asked.

As I walked across the room to the refrigerator, he said, "Relationships are never only about love, you know. They're also about power. If one person in a relationship has less power than the other, it seldom works."

"That doesn't make any sense," I said. "We get along really well most of the time, and you have all the power here."

He looked startled. "I have all the power?" he said.

"You've got all the money," I said.

"That's only one kind of power," he explained. "Men need women more than women need men, that's power. You're young, and pretty, that's another kind of power. You're smart and competent. You understand things better than I do, and you can even fix TV's and fix my broken glasses. All of that is power."

"Well, if I have all this power, why do I have to do all this work?" I asked him laughing.

He was still serious when he explained. "Competence is like money, if you have more of it, you have to share more of it."

"That sounds like a lose, lose," I said. "I learn more so I have to do more?'

He nodded. "Men don't have any clue about how women feel in the world until they're over 50," he said.

"How did you figure that one out?" I asked.

"Well, when a man is over fifty, he sees other younger men rising at work, he feels the loss of his physical power, and he starts to sense the fear and loss of confidence that women have known their whole lives. Age evens things up."

"Men still have an edge," I said.

"Not always," he explained. "Did you ever see a young Italian couple when they first get married? He's all about being the tough guy. 'I'm the boss,' and she's all about 'Yes, Boss.' Then fast forward 40 years, and he's walking behind her, asking her 'What should we do mama? Where are we going?'"

I laughed. "That would be why?" I asked.

"Because women have a different kind of power than men," Mario said. "They spend years building up their inside strength, their emotional strength. They take responsibility for the kids, the house, they make a million small decisions every day that take smart thinking and they have to do it in a split second. They keep their kids from killing each other, they have to know when to take a kid to the hospital, and they have to make their husbands feel desirable and welcome. They keep the home safe. A man just goes to work, does his job, and comes home. Men have power in the outer world. But once that world shuts them out, they don't have anything to fall back on and a lot of years they have nothing to do. A woman has skills she's built up over a lifetime. Emotional muscle, inner strength. A man has no such skills."

"So how come there's not equal pay? Why do men have such an edge? That makes no sense."

"You're right," Mario said. "That's what I'm saying. Women are fighting for something that they've already got. As soon as they figure it out, men become extinct. Especially now, with computers."

"I think you under rate men," I said. "They have more to offer than you think."

He made a face. "Then why are you always reproaching me?"

"I never reproach you," I said. "I always just try to communicate with you so we can have a better relationship. There's nothing you ever want to change about me?"

Mario looked at me but said nothing.

I watched him and then said, "Come on. Be brave..."

"Well," he said, softly, slowly, "If you have a flaw...I mean I'm just saying 'if' you have a flaw...it might be that you lack patience."

"That's it?" I said, laughing. "That's all you've got? With all my virtues?"

Mario looked serious. "It's only a matter of time," he said. "Before women find out what a bad deal marriage is. Then we'll see what happens."

Chapter 17

January started out in Vegas again, but we didn't stay for long. After 3 days Mario and I flew to LA for meetings with producers, directors and others in the "movie business."

We stayed at the Beverly Hills Hotel, a stark pink and green stucco building, with over the top service and a real red carpet under the awning at the entrance to the hotel. Lots of pink flamingo statues decorated the lush green landscape. Several of Mario's old friends came by and over the next couple of weeks, he took meetings with those in the business who could "green light" a movie as well as some producers who wanted to put together a "package" and wanted him to write a screenplay for them.

But even doing business, Mario liked to play. He truly enjoyed the glitz and the glamour but was always very mindful of the fact that it was just play. Life was serious business. What we were doing was not, he often told me when we travelled.

The Polo Lounge, the setting for many Hollywood movies, was in the Beverly Hills Hotel, and at the Polo Lounge, you could find yourself sitting next to all kinds of celebrities.

"I probably wouldn't even know them," I told Mario.

He laughed, "Don't worry, Lanetta will point them out."

The suite at that hotel was bright and airy, still lots of French Provincial furniture and marble top tables, but less ornate than the European Hotels we'd stayed at and so, more comfortable for me. But the beds weren't. Europe, with all their down comforters, couch cushions and pillows had Hollywood beat.

The morning after we arrived, we woke to the sound of lots of waiters and waitresses, valets and housekeepers buzzing around the hallways outside our room. By the time we were up and dressed, Mario was dying to get out and have a great breakfast and take me out shopping again.

By the time Lanetta came over to take us walking around Santa Monica and back to Georgio's on Rodeo Drive, I was determined to enjoy myself. Both of them were so excited to show me around, that I felt I owed them at least that!

Mario took me to visit the Paramount lot to show me the building in which he wrote The Godfather script. I had fun that day, because I loved how excited Mario was about all of it. I loved that he so underestimated his own importance, that he became that kid who grew up in Hell's kitchen and wanted to share "Hollywood" with me.

It wasn't long before Mario got restless again, and we were off to Vegas. This time to the Desert Inn. I didn't like the Desert Inn as much as the Sands. It was too impersonal, somehow colder, and so after two days, we were out of there.

By the time we were on the plane flying home to New York again, we were both laughing because it was such a relief to be going home. To live in our own houses, and be back in our own domains, surrounded by those we were used to, those who were used to us.

"I can't wait to wake up in my own bed tomorrow," I told him.

"Honey," he said, with a smile. "I can't wait to be home either. To be able to get up in the middle of the night and fry a potato and egg omelet with no one around to tell me it's not good for me."

"Thank God," I told him. "I agree. It's impossible to try to keep you healthy against your will. Too much responsibility."

"Isn't this perfect?" he said. "We have the best of both worlds."

"It is," I said. "I love travelling around with you sometimes, but even more I love coming home."

The year before, by some magic of hard work and great good luck, I had finally finished the manuscript of the book I was writing. Mario was right, it was tougher than I imagined. I struggled with each sentence, each paragraph, each page. As I wrote, I could see the patients I'd loved and lost. I could remember how they smelled and could still hear their voices. I was enraged again by all the injustices and harm that medicine had caused. I grieved again for each of them. I could also see my place in my personal defeats. I was far away enough to analyze it, but still close enough to feel the pain. I kept remembering Mario telling me, "Show don't tell," and so I did. But Technicolor multimedia memories take their toll. My emotions were raw. In the end, I finally got it all down. I was true to myself, true to my patients, and true to my passion. But it beat the hell out of me and I was glad to have been able to get it out of my head and onto the pages.

Mario said, "I'll send it to Candida, my agent, and we'll see if she thinks another agent will want to represent you."

"I don't want anyone to do me any favors because of you," I told him.

He smiled. "Don't worry," he said. "We're talking about a blood thirsty lot here. It's money that means something. Not friendship. If they think they can make some money on you, they'll give it a shot, if they don't see it, you're dead."

"Can't I just send it out to a publisher myself?" I asked him.

"It's as hard or harder to get an agent than it is to get a book published," he said. "No matter how many stories you read about undiscovered talent, from the slush pile, few editors will even read a manuscript if an agent hasn't gone through it first."

"Mario," I said, "I'm not even sure what an agent is. I don't know what a publisher is, or what an editor does. I don't have a clue about any of it."

He laughed. "That's the easy part," he said. "That's business, not art. An agent is the person who first reads your book, and decides if it can make anybody or everybody some money. If you're lucky enough to find an agent to represent you, then you've already gotten to first base. That agent, if she's been around a while, has relationships built up with certain editors from certain publishing houses."

"What's the difference between an editor and a publisher?"

"A publisher is the company represented by some main guy or gal. She runs the business. An editor is the one who first gets the book from an agent, either believes in it or not, and works out the numbers to see if it can make the publisher money. If that editor thinks it can, and she believes in it enough, she meets with the publisher and pitches your book. Then the publisher decides."

"That's a lot of people to go through before a book gets into a bookstore isn't it?"

Mario laughed. "That's why I said writing is too tough a job if you can do anything else. You got to have to write or have something really important to say."

"I'm already discouraged," I told him.

"You'll be okay," he said. "You're a terrific nurse. You got a backup plan. You don't need writing to feed your family."

"I don't want some agent representing me because of you," I told him. "I want an agent to represent my book because they love it."

He looked at me, with a certain kindness when he said, "That's not how it works. You've got to get an agent to read it first. An author, any author, can use all the help he can get."

"But I want it to be about me, not because I know you," I told him.

"Don't worry about it," he said, "Publishing is a dirty business. If it's no good, whether you know me or not, no agent will represent you, no editor will read it, and no publisher will want it."

"Okay," I said. "That makes me feel better.

Mario laughed. "It shouldn't," he said.

I mailed my finished manuscript to his agent, Candida, and once she'd read the manuscript, she offered to represent me.

"I don't want her to do it just as a kindness," I said.

Mario said, "It's publishing. I told you writing is a brutal business. Take any kindness you can get. Don't worry. If it's not a good book, the readers won't buy it or read it. Only then will you know what kind of book you've written."

Once back home again on Long Island, Mario and I got back to writing again. He was working on a new screenplay called "The Cotton Club" for Bob Evans, and I was waiting anxiously to find out what was happening with my book.

Candida really did get right back to us. She said she'd called Joni Evans of Linden Press, a part of Simon & Shuster, and Joni wanted the book. She was willing to give me a $6,500 advance but the manuscript had to be edited down. It was far too many pages.

Mario came over and tried to talk me down.

"I can't believe it. Writing pays less than nursing," I said. "I worked on that book for almost two years, and they want to chop it apart."

Mario laughed. "Honey," he said, "You said you wanted to get the word out. Simon & Schuster is a good house; Joni is smart and a really good editor. An advance is only money they give you up front. You still have to pay it back out of your royalties. If it sells, you're in the clear right out of the gate. If it doesn't, you'll owe a lot less. What you don't make on this book, you'll make on the next. It's always a gamble."

"So, I should say yes?" I asked.

"It will get you into the game," he said. "If you're lucky, you'll make a little money. And you'll start another book."

The following weeks, I went into New York City to meet my editors, Joni Evans and Marjorie Williams. Joni was tough and smart. Marjorie was softer, but still firm. I really liked them, though more than once with one slash of a pen, they cut me to the quick. I felt like they were not only cutting my book, they were amputating it. Still, both were smart and funny professionals, so I took a deep breath, accepted what I could, and then tried to let the rest go. When they said they wanted more direct teaching, and that the manuscript would have to be cut a lot, I knew I was going to have a really hard time with the editing business. It would have to be cut by at least half, Joni guessed. Of course, she was right. 750 pages was just too many pages.

I was horrified. "Well, don't cut the info the patients need," I told them. "Cut the personal stuff."

They smiled and agreed.

The moment I signed the contract, I began choosing the pieces I thought should be cut and I began the rewrite, but Joni and Marjorie had a cleaver much bigger than mine.

Once I realized how painful it was for me to let go, I started seriously studying Buddhism and all the other Eastern Religions. I began to meditate. It seemed the only intelligent thing to do. I had to learn to stop all this damn suffering, especially when I knew I should be elated. "My book is being picked up, it's going to be published," I kept saying to myself.

"You don't know how lucky you are," Marjorie told me. "Very few new authors have captured the imagination of a publishing house. This book does that. Everyone's excited about it."

I began to meditate more often and longer. Something was going to have to help me get a grip. By now I knew it wasn't going to be my mind!

Mario left for LA to finish the second draft of The Cotton Club two weeks later. He had a professional typist out there, Vikki, who knew screenplay formatting, was pleasant, professional and fast. He said it was much quicker to fly out to LA, than to try to have it typed back home.

"I can learn the formatting," I told him.

He frowned. "I thought you wanted to be a writer," he said. "Stop fooling around and write."

So when he went away, I kept rewriting every day, trying to do what they called a structural rewrite, and several times, when I had to go to NY to work with Marjorie, I took my sister Bibs with me as a buffer.

The line editing was even tougher than the cuts. I had to fight over keeping my voice. I'd write, "Me, who was scared shitless, of everything." They would change it to "I, who was scared shitless of everything."

I spent those weeks in a fury. Mario and I talked several times each day, and as soon as he flew back, he came right over to see me. I poured out all my frustrations over the book, the editing, the time, the worry, the work. He sat on my couch and listened. Didn't say anything.

"What?" I said. "You think I'm crazy?"

He shook his head. "No," he said, "On my second book, "The Fortunate Pilgrim, the editor changed my voice. Must have been a college professor. I hated it."

"What did you do?" I asked.

"Took my book back. Took it away from the publishing house. Put it in the trunk of my car and kept it there for four years," he said. "By the time I sent it out again, I realized I could say no to some changes, but had to allow others."

"I mean when that book was published, was it better?" I asked.

"It didn't make me any money, though it was declared a minor classic," he said.

"So, was it worth it?" I asked.

"Depends," he said. "It was worth it to me. If I had let them do what they wanted, it could have been published four years earlier but not the way I wanted it. I'm a writer and it was my book."

Mario was always calm and comforting when he was reassuring me, but it was a very different thing when it had to do with his writing. But only with his writing!

When Mario came back from LA after the second draft of The Cotton Club, he was at the very least agitated. He wanted me to read what had been done to his screenplay.

"Evans is changing it," he said. "With a title like The Cotton Club it should be a musical. It should be a buddy movie like Butch Cassidy and the Sundance Kid. Instead, he wants it to be another gangster movie!"

"That seems like a jump," I said. "I don't know anything about it so I can't follow. What's the connection?"

Mario lit another cigar. Whenever Mario was thinking, he either lit or smoked a foot-long cigar. "Well, in the early twenties, The Cotton Club was owned by a New York gangster, Owen Madden. He sold booze there to the whites all through prohibition. Because of his connections with politicians, they turned a blind eye. But the big thing about the Cotton Club for me, was the music. Duke Ellington, Cab Callaway, and Ethel Waters. It was a big blues and jazz place."

"That's why he thought about you," I said. "But what interested you about it?"

"The relationship between the white owner and his black friend, the dancer. There was such segregation at the time, that this friendship was my idea of a good buddy movie," he said. "That's what interested me."

I read it again then, and had to admit I thought Mario was right. "Thing is," I told him, "You're a brand right now and people who want to see your movies, want to see gangsters."

Mario was silent. That was not good news. It meant he hated the compromise.

"I wish you could argue the way I can," I told him. "It would do your heart good." But he thought of himself as a reasonable, civilized man so he was more than polite whenever he spoke to any of the movie people.

Still after a few more conversations, he was so upset, we had to run off to Vegas again. The Sands again this time. But even after winning at Baccarat, even after a great meal of his favorite Chinese food, when we got back to the suite, he couldn't shake his mood. He was silent and sullen.

For a long time I said nothing. Then as we got into bed, I tried, "Maybe you could think of it as The Gun and The Cotton Club."

He laid down in bed, but then he sat up like a shot, and pulled a big long cigar out of the bedside stand. He lit it and began to chew and puff.

Finally, I couldn't stand it another minute. I jumped up too, grabbed him by the shoulders and shook him. "Look," I said. "If you're going to take a million dollars, you've got to turn a few extra tricks!!"

Mario looked at me and started to laugh. He laughed and laughed. "You're right," he said. "You really are right!"

"It's not that bad," I said. "It's really not."

He relaxed. "Give them time," he said. "They're not finished with it. They'll destroy it yet."

Chapter 18

It was May by the time all the editing on my book was done, and time to fly to Cannes again. We left for Paris on the Concord, which would cut flying time to three hours instead of more than 8. It was an experience of a lifetime, Mario said.

But once we were on that plane we both realized it would also be a very sleek, very narrow, very noisy three hours which homogenized my blood cells and destroyed my inner ear so that I felt miserable when we arrived.

Mario had gotten us a suite at The Grande Hotel, and it was beautiful. It overlooked the rich blue Mediterranean, and the breeze coming in from the balcony was sweet smelling and warm. I laid down on the bed, and tried to rest, but something was wrong.

That night I forced myself to go out to eat at one of the small places on the Promenade, but I couldn't even order anything. Then we went over to the Palais (the big casino) to gamble for a couple of hours. But I couldn't stay long.

Besides, Mario had a meeting in the morning with Bob Evans, so we went to bed early. But I couldn't sleep. I woke up with chills, nauseated, and in pain. My back hurt and my head was spinning. I let Mario sleep but when he woke up that morning, I said, "Something's physically wrong with me. I'm sick and I don't know what it is. So, you're going to have to go by yourself. Sorry."

Mario looked concerned. "Want me to get you a doctor?" he asked.

"No," I said. "Go to your meeting. If I'm still sick when you get back, we'll think about it."

"You sure?" he asked.

"I'm sure," I said. "When I'm dying I prefer to be alone."

"You are a funny little thing," he said. "Want me to order up some tea and scones for you before I go?"

I kept dozing off. "No," I said. "If I need anything I can call room service. Just go. Good luck."

The phone rang as soon as Mario closed the door.

It was Marjorie Williams. "The Book of the Month Club and The Literary Guild are both bidding on your book," she said. "Closing figure today was $17,500 by Book of the Month. It started off at $5000."

My back really hurt. "Great!" I said, but my head was spinning. I didn't know what it meant. What I did know was that I was feeling really awful. Marjorie said that the clubs were willing to pay more for my book than they had offered Cheever, Tyler, and Godwin. I wished that meant I was a better writer than they were.

As soon as I got off the phone, I started to shake and shiver uncontrollably. I didn't know what to do, so I got out of bed, wrapped the comforter around me and stumbled into the bathroom. Then what did I do? I sat on the floor and cried. I laid down on the cold hard tile and rolled around back and forth until I was so dizzy I couldn't think. Still some thoughts snuck in. I was in really bad pain, my back was threatening to crack in half. I didn't want to die in Cannes with no family or friends around. I prayed, then I screamed, cursed and finally passed out cold wrapped in that down comforter in the middle of the world.

When I woke up, the pain was so bad I almost passed out again, but I managed to struggle and try to stand up. Suddenly, I got it! A kidney stone!! I had only one moment to sit down and digest that, wondering how I missed diagnosing it earlier when one clink, and there went the stone. Wow! Pain gone. Cured. My last thought before I fell back onto the bed again was, "I don't want to do this again. Not alone. Not even on the French Riviera.

The phone woke me up. It was Marjorie. "The Book of the month won," she announced. "It went 9 rounds, for $22,500. Congratulations!"

"Thanks," I said. "Congratulations to you too."

The following six months Mario and I flew back and forth between New York, Las Vegas and Los Angeles. While I was struggling with the rewrites on my book tentatively titled "The Nurse's Tale" and negotiating plans for publicity and touring, Mario was working on his screenplay.

"But Mario," I argued. "They want me to fly cross country to 14 cities and do newspaper, radio and TV in all these different places. Did you know they don't even pay for that? I mean they pay for the travelling and the hotels and the meals, but you don't get paid to be on TV or anything like that."

Mario nodded. "Yes," he said. "I knew it."

"Is that why you don't do publicity?" I asked him. "Is that why you don't tour?"

"No," he said. "I'm not a good talker. I'm not good on camera. I'm not like you. I can't sell my books."

"But I failed public speaking," I said. "How do we even know I can do it? What if I make a mess of it?"

He laughed. "You won't," he said. "Somebody will ask you a question that annoys you or gets you started, and there will be no stopping you. Besides the camera will love you."

"Well, maybe I can just shut my eyes, and some angel will just take care of the interviews," I said.

Mario just smiled and shook his head. "You'll be fine," he said.

Though Mario would never admit it, a big hook for him was my spiritual beliefs—the world that was a big part of my life but one in which Mario swore he didn't believe. An Italian who doesn't believe? Italians are steeped in miracles and myth cause most of them are Catholic. "So you don't believe in Satan, or in the devil?" I asked him.

"I believe there's evil in the world," he said. "But human evil."

"What about God and angels?" I asked.

"How can a smart girl like you believe in that stuff?" he asked again.

"How can a smart man like you, not?" I countered. "It seems to me that if I'm wrong, I'll never know. After I'm dead if you're right, my consciousness will disappear and all of me will be gone. I'll be extinct. If I'm right and some part of us remains, I'll have made my life a lot easier. Why would you give that up?"

"It defies reason," is what he said.

"Reason is all that you are? The rest of life is reasonable according to you? Ah...you and I live in such different worlds," I told him. "My belief in something greater than myself includes more than reason for that's such a small aspect of mind. I've seen too many miracles to believe only in reason. You've never seen a miracle?"

"Sure," he said. "The way my life turned out. But I figure I was just lucky. A big part of life is getting lucky."

"What about a soul? What part of you drives you to write? Does that rest on reason?"

"No," he said. "That's my personal insanity. I feel I can't live if I don't write."

"Soul purpose is what I call that," I said. "Not reason."

He treated my stories of God and angels with both awe and amusement but I know it gave him comfort. I'd shared stories of the miracles in my life with him, and though he had no explanation for them, he still resisted believing. I watched him relax with my stories, and sometimes even give them some thought. In that part of my world there was protection, kindness, truth and heavenly justice. Just like in his Olympian myths and his Godfather book.

He said he thought I was crazy but he did admit that no one else he knew could navigate the world with such competence and so he allowed that my belief system served me.

For himself, he put my truth in the place of ancient myth and fable. It was in myth that he felt the safety of white magic which cradled him in the arms of story and hid us all from the unkind realities of life.

One night after we'd had a long talk about our different beliefs, I asked him, "Mario, as an aside, why don't you ever say you love me?"

He shook his head and looked at me. Then he admitted, "Because every one I love dies."

I frowned. "You mean Erika, and your brother Gino, and ...."

Mario said, "and others..."

I laughed. Automatically I said, "You mean you think your magic is stronger than my magic??"

"I don't know," he said. "Can't take a chance. Don't like to tempt the Fates."

I shook my head. "Be brave," I said. "Take a chance. My angels are always at the ready." Then I pointed out many of the miracle stories in my life I had told him before.

He tousled my hair then and smiled. "You're a brave girl," he said.

It wasn't too long after that, that in a fall to innocence or a moment of forgetting, he said, "I love you," and I knew he had begun to trust a little more in my universe.

That year was filled with confusion and bedlam as well as excitement. In other words, it was complete craziness. But I found out more about the publishing world than I ever thought existed. And even more about what authors had to do to help a book sell.

I was interviewed by People magazine, had tons of photos taken, and did more cross-country interviews than I could even imagine. Linden Press ran ads for me in the New York Times as well as the Nursing magazines. On the day the People magazine article came out, Joni had to take the book back for another printing. The book had sold out.

The end of that year, while everyone else was celebrating at a huge party in the ballroom of the Sands, with streamers and colored confetti, while they were drinking and dancing to music played by a huge band, and eating more food than anyone could eat, Mario and I stayed by ourselves in a suite called Secretariat. At midnight, we watched the ball drop in Times Square on TV. Then, we both called home to talk to the kids and wish them a Happy New Year.

Chapter 19

After I finished touring twenty one cities to promote The Nurse's Story, and it had gone back for six printings, I had to decide how to handle publicity for the foreign editions. England and nine other foreign countries had bought the rights to my book, and I had to do some publicity for the English version of The Nurse's Story.

That spring Mario and I flew the Concord again and stayed at the Dorchester, Mario's very favorite hotel in the whole world.

This time we even had "high tea" in the afternoon, complete with the piano player in the main lobby. Everyone was dressed to the nine's in clothes that reminded me of the Great Gatsby. Only the quietest hum of conversation, no loud voices.

Large silver trays carried Wedgewood china teapots and cups with saucers, and the tiniest tray of crustless sandwiches cut in quarters filled with cucumbers, or cream cheese and scallions, egg salad, or smoked salmon. My favorite was plain watercress on buttered bread. Carts were wheeled or trays carried by waiters in black tuxedos and brought to the small glass or marble covered tables in front of the tufted chairs in which we sat.

Of course, I put milk in my Darjeeling tea which was all wrong, and Mario asked for seconds on the sandwiches, which either horrified or amused the waiter. But the English are so deadpan that we never would have known.

I'm not a big fan of going crazy over food, even dessert—but the scones with clotted cream and strawberry jam were good enough to make me travel back to the Dorchester time and again.

Italians cover long tables with so much food that it has to spill over the edges of any dish, and there can't be any space between those dishes; they like the look of more than enough food—so everyone can carry some home. By comparison, the classy English tea sandwiches looked special, rare, exquisite. They were so tiny, they forced even me to long for more. I never thought tea in the afternoon could be romantic, but that day was crazy silly fun.

During that stay in England we met with our foreign agent Deborah Rogers, and the head of my English publisher, Collins, to work on the editing and cover design of the English edition of The Nurse's Story and also a couple of taped film interviews for TV, plus a print interview for the London Times and a couple of radio shows.

That was necessary if I was to sign a foreign rights contract for my next book. I was still touring and doing publicity for The Nurse's Story in the U.S., had fought the battles I had to over fiction/nonfiction as well as over the cover design and had finally won the battle to call my book The Nurse's Story rather than The Nurse's Tale. No small thing because while Joni and Marge were imagining a classy Chaucerian tale, I was imagining the latest ads for stewardesses which screamed "fly me." Bad for the Image of Nurses. One slip of the pen and it could be "The Nurse's Tail."

Deborah told me that The Nurse's Story also sold to Portugal, Israel, and the contract for Spain was in the works.

Mario and I had several other meetings at fancy English restaurants like the White Elephant in London while the publishers were discussing promotion plans for The Nurse's Story and the options for my new book.

The most interesting dinner we had was at the Tai Pan restaurant, and though I usually love Chinese food, this food was too spicy for me. But the head of Pan Publishing, which was the paperback house that bought my book, Sonny Mehta and his wife Gita, were really fun. They were both smart and interesting and broke through all the stereotypes I had about people from India. Gita had written a book called Karma Kola, and she summed up everything in that book about canned spirituality. I loved hearing her speak. Both were animated and great conversationalists and so for once, I had a really good time.

That night we got back to the hotel and there was a message that I had an early evening interview with Jane Savidge from "Nursing Times." I had spoken to her a few times and she was very savvy about the problems all nurses had and was thrilled to be doing the interview with me. I was looking forward to it.

When Mario and I got up the following morning, it was so rainy and dreary that Mario decided to stay in the hotel and work while I took an hour trying to get some makeup on, choose the right clothes, and get my very straight hair to even bend in a curl. I was truly so uncomfortable being on any kind of film, it took everything I had to muster up the courage to do it. I made it just in time to run into the car Collins had sent to pick me up.

I got through the interviews. I really got into it, because I finally understood that even though England had Universal Health Care, most of their nurses had many of the same problems we had in the U.S. So when each interviewer asked a question that touched a real problem, I was just on automatic pilot. I went on an impassioned plea to save the nurses, so they could save the patients. The interviewers loved that they didn't even have to prompt me with too many questions, and we filled both film reels and article pages without any effort.

It was a really dreary English day. When I jumped into the taxi to get back to the Dorchester, it was raining so hard that I didn't even have time to open the umbrella that I held in my hand. The driver was kind and courteous, but water was dripping off my hair and down my neck as I got into the cab. By the time I arrived back at the Dorchester, I was acutely aware of the sloshing of my shoes as I ran through the lobby of the hotel to get to the elevators.

There was a tall blond man standing in front of the elevator, and I could see by the light above that he had already pushed the button. Still, I walked in front of him and pushed it again. He smiled.

"I can't believe it. Any time I have to do an interview of any kind, I swear it rains. It happens too often to be a coincidence," I said. "You can't imagine what a pain in the ass that is."

He smiled. "I can," he said.

Something about him seemed familiar. His uniform, dark blue with fancy gold buttons and epaulettes made him look like some kind of dignitary, but he could as easily have been a doorman in that hotel.

He held his hand against the elevator door when it opened to let me in first.

"Thanks," I said. "You know, I get how important publicity is, especially when you want people to know about a book you've written, but I do think there has to be an easier way. Oh, sorry I'm just winding down. Interviews make me nervous." I stopped and took a deep breath. "My name's Carol," I told him.

He looked shy. "Chris," he said, and smiled again.

He got off on the floor below mine. When the doors opened, and he was leaving, he turned and said, "Good luck with your book."

"Thanks," I said. "I'm sure it will be okay. Nice meeting you."

It was only in that small space of time, as the elevator was closing, and I watched him walk down the hall, that it hit me! I know him. I know who he is! Oh God, I thought, I am just never going to get it.

When Mario opened the door to the suite, I said, "You'll never guess who I met in the elevator. You won't believe it. I think it was Christopher Walken. I thought he was the doorman."

Mario laughed. "I believe you," he said. "I saw him in the lobby yesterday."

"Mario," I said, "You have no clue how crazy making this is for me. It's all like a half-remembered dream. I keep seeing people I think I know. I mean really know and I try to remember where I met them, only to find out they're familiar cause I've seen them on screen, not in person."

He laughed. "You'll get used to it," he said.

"I mean it really is like 'all the World's a Stage...and we, but different players on it.' Nerve racking."

"That's a good idea for a movie," Mario said laughing.

Chapter 20

It was in Las Vegas that year when I began to write my next book, "Rusty's Story." It was the story of a young girl with epilepsy who had been locked up in a mental institution because she had been misdiagnosed as paranoid schizophrenic. When I met her, she was 19, and I took her home to live with me and the kids. I knew that one of the reasons she had spent her teenage years in a mental institution was because her family was poor, and they had no one to advocate for them. I hated that she had lost all that time in her young life because of human error and a dysfunctional system. I knew we had to get more information out there so it wouldn't happen to anyone else. I was passionate and determined to let everyone know the traps in the health care system so they could protect themselves and the people they loved.

After that trip Mario seriously began working on his book "The Sicilian."

He had a whole process when he was writing a book. When he had enough pages to put into chapters, he sorted his chapters by number and put each chapter in a separate colored folder. On the front of each folder, he wrote scenes that he'd set, the characters who appeared, and what was happening in that chapter. Once he had enough folders, all different colors, he began writing those chapters on huge white oaktag posters and hanging them all over his walls. Every wall was covered. Then he'd lay on his couch or sit in his chair and study the whole panorama. It was from those charts and the scenes that showed up in his mind, that he created his stories.

We had been home on Long Island for only two months when Mario announced, "Well, it's time to go to the charts with the characters," he said. "Let's see if we can see a story that interests us."

So we began to gather all his folders together, copy them on oaktag, and tack them on the walls in his study.

When we were finished, Mario took a long hard look, squinted and said, "I have a lot of work to do. Time to get away again."

"Back to Vegas?" I asked.

"Let's see if we can get lucky," he said. "We've been working too much. Need to give some space for fresh ideas to grow."

After a few days in Vegas, we flew to LA to stay at the Beverly Hills Hotel. I had meetings set up with another nurse author, Barbara Huttman, who had written the book "Code Blue" which was released at the same time as The Nurse's Story.

While Mario was meeting with Bob Evans again to talk about "The Cotton Club" and some of the other Hollywood producers to accept or reject any new deals, I asked Barbara to meet me at the hotel so we could join forces for nursing. The Nurse's Story was getting more press, was more popular and had sold more books, but Barbara's book got better reviews from the nursing critics and academics.

She was tall, funny and smart. I was as thrilled to meet her as she was to meet me. We sat for hours, discussing the critical situation with health care, determined to help each other in any way we could with our books. We also talked about Echo Heron, another nurse who was writing books to help inform the public. Each of us offered to write to any magazine or newspaper which reviewed our books, to champion each other and share the fact that nurses were speaking out, for the patients. Barbara was tickled to death by the pink Hotel, The Polo lounge, room service and of course by meeting Mario.

While we were there, Marjorie called and told me I was booked for AM San Francisco and LA as well as another big show in Detroit on Jan. 27th. I still had several shows left to do in California.

That night, Mario and I went to dinner at Polo Lounge with Barbara, Vicki—Mario's screenplay typist—Lanetta, and some of Mario's old friends from Brooklyn who had moved to California. Josh Greenfeld, who wrote "Harry and Tonto", and then the 'Noah' books about his autistic son, and his wife Foumi—a true artist in her own right—were two of my favorite people. I loved that about Mario, he kept all his old friends and loved sharing everything he had with them.

A few days later, we flew first class back to JFK in New York, and sitting right behind me the whole way, was Jon Voight, the only actor who ever impressed me. I just loved Midnight Cowboy and never got over it. Still, I had such a horror of intruding, when I finally stood up and saw him, I just smiled and said, "Hi," as though I'd known him forever.

Whenever I was home in NY, my gang of nursing buddies, Bridie, Maureen, and Wanda met at my house to discuss how Healthcare was getting even crazier, and what we could do about it. Those nurses and those subjects were ones I wrote about in my books.

The following week, Mario and I went to New York City to have dinner with Christopher McElhose, the chief editor from Collins in England.

That following day, Candida called to tell me my book, "The Nurse's Story", had also sold to Holland, Portugal and Israel. Marjorie Williams called to tell me the book went back for a fourth printing. They're printing 4500 more copies but they cut my percentage to 13% and raised the price of the book to $15.95.

When I told Mario, "Joni told me they don't want me to think they're hustling me."

Mario said, "Why not? They are. Still, they're selling your books."

It was a crazy whirlwind of a time. I woke up each morning not knowing what the day was going to offer. One night at 11pm, CNN sent a limo for me. A study had been published in the "Post" that United Press picked up, which said that 8% of nurses had given a narcotic overdose to a dying patient. I knew I had to go in and fight for Patient Choice or I had to stop complaining about it. The President of the American Nurses Association was also going to be on the show. Still, somebody had to represent the nurses in the trenches and the patients in the beds.

To my surprise, the show went well. But now it was even more important for me to get out there. I could see there was big trouble in the profession, because the nursing organizations couldn't hear what working nurses were saying.

Within the month, I went into the city to meet with the Bantam people about the paperback publication of my book, "The Nurse's Story." Jack Romanos, Linda Grey, and the man who would be my greatest support from the publicity department, Matthew Scher, were there. They were all really good people and seemed to understand what I was trying to do.

Jack said The Nurse's Story would be their Super Release for October. But they insisted I tour again. I told them I'd have to take my sister, Bibs, with me. I wasn't willing to spend 24 days of eating alone in strange hotels and restaurants. I was so happy when they agreed, that it broke down all my defenses.

The other big battle I had to fight, was that Bantam asked Mario for a quote to put on the cover of the paperback edition of my book. "It helps a lot because of name recognition," Matthew told me.

Mario graciously wrote the quote for the Bantam edition. "A shattering, exhilarating book. A tribute to human dignity and courage."

When I got home, Mario called. "How did it go?" he asked.

"It went okay," I said. "But they told me they asked you for a quote for the cover of my book. That doesn't make sense to me. If it was a book on criminals or the mafia, you'd be an expert. Why would anyone believe that you were an expert on nursing?" I asked.

"Experience. Because I saw nurses in action," he said calmly, "Because I think they're important. You saved me on the first night you came to help my wife."

I felt bad that I had even questioned him. "Thanks for the quote," I said. "but I wanted to do this alone."

"You will," Mario said, laughing. "I won't give you a quote for your other books. All the rest you can do alone."

When my book hit the Bestseller lists, I got flowers and telegrams from Collins Publishers, in England, Marjorie Chapman and Christopher McElhose, as well as from my publishers here and all my friends in the US.

But on the night everyone came to my house to drink champagne and celebrate with me because my book had become a best seller, I had to sneak into the bathroom to cry. It wasn't that I wasn't grateful, because I was.

I really couldn't celebrate my victory without remembering all those patients who had shared themselves with me. Their lives were the lives that I'd written about, those ordinary people who lived and died in such extraordinary ways. I had loved them. And on that night, I really missed them.

The following week, Candida called. She'd sent my second book "Rusty's Story" out to editors. "Epilepsy and misdiagnosis isn't as sexy as other subjects," she said. So Rusty didn't have as large a target audience as The Nurse's Story. But she agreed, the offer from the publishers was even worse news than she thought. They only wanted to give me $20,000 for Rusty and that in 3 payments. I told Candida I'd think about it. But I wouldn't really think about anything less than $30,000.

I called Mario and ran right over to his house.

Upstairs in his study, I just kept shaking my head in disbelief as I explained, "I know need shouldn't be the criteria, but I've already made them over $55,000 in reprint money alone. They tell me the publisher has to make at least a 15% profit on every book. They're paying me only 7.5% and 10% for the paperback reprint rights. They're making a lot of money on The Nurse's Story. I also toured and did a lot of work for no money."

"How much did you get for The Nurse's Story advance?" he asked.

"You know how much I got," I said. "$6500."

Mario smiled. "They're offering you 5 times as much," he said. "So, you're on a winning streak. Is money why you wrote the book?"

"Of course not," I said. "You know I wrote it to tell people how important nurses are, and to help the patients know what goes on behind the scenes of hospitals."

How many books have you sold?" he asked, lighting one of his cigars.

"I think they sold out all the hard back books that they printed and Linda Grey, my editor at Bantam, said they were going to make it their Super Release and start the print run at 600,000."

"Didn't your book sell to the book clubs too?" he asked.

"Yes," I said.

"It got on the best seller lists?" he asked.

"Yes," I said.

"Your book is doing what you want it to do, right?" he asked.

"When you put it that way," I said.

"Stop worrying about all this bullshit," he said. "If you're a writer, you have to write. Just keep writing. One day maybe you'll get lucky."

The following months seemed to fly by. I signed the contract and got the payments from Bantam. Also, Finland bought the book, and so did, Norway and Israel.

Mario and I continued working on his book 'The Sicilian' and I continued working on 'Rusty's Story'. Often, whenever we were together, Mario tried to teach me screenplay structure. But I just wasn't good at writing short.

"Okay," he said. "So that just proves you're a novelist," he said. "You're a fiction writer—a storyteller. Might as well stick to your strength. Though, if I had to depend on only books for a living, I'd still be starving. It's my movies that save me."

Chapter 21

Whenever Mario was writing, he lived in his story. His whole perspective on Life changed, and reality was Background. That meant he rarely spoke during the day, had nightmares and was possessed by all the torments of each of his characters. So, it was understandable that every couple of weeks, he'd have to run away and escape to safety—out of his study, away from his characters, away from his typewriter. For me, it meant away from my family, away from my friends, and away from my safe place, home.

The last months had been completely crazy for me, and I felt as though I escaped rather than left my house freely this time. There were loose ends all over the place. Still, when Mario was ready to go, I had one choice: Be ready to go with him, or stay home without him.

This time we were going to London, England, again.

I was barely settled in the limo on our way to the airport, when Mario handed me the airline tickets and asked, as he always had, "Did you check your passport?"

"Why?" I asked, "I mean for what?"

"To make sure you brought it," he said.

I rummaged through my pocketbook to find it. Then I quickly thumbed through it. But this time as I looked over the dates I couldn't believe my eyes. It had expired! Two days before! I made a face and sighed.

"What's wrong?" Mario asked.

"Oh God," I said. "I don't know how to tell you this...but it's expired."

Mario was silent. I held my breath. Mario was often silent, but this wasn't a good silence.

"What are we going to do?" I asked.

"You know what Freud said," he told me. "There are no accidents. This probably was your way of telling me you really didn't want to go with me."

Suddenly, I was in a fury. I was mad at myself for not checking to make sure my passport was valid, I was mad at Mario for telling me that I really didn't want to go, and I was frustrated because I couldn't figure out what to do about it.

We were already on the way to the airport. "Why would you automatically assume I was being passive resistant?" I asked. "That's not my style. I'm up front about what I don't want to do, where I don't want to go. Why would I try to trick you?"

"Unconsciously, you don't want to go," he said with certainty.

"Stop saying that," I said. "How can you tell me what I really want to do? How can you know me better than I do?"

"It's not me," he said. "It's Freud. And, it's obvious."

"You're making me want to kill you," I told him. "That doesn't help me problem-solve about what we're going to do to work this thing out. I need to concentrate on how we're going to get to England."

He looked at me, surprised. "We?" he said. "I've got my ticket and my passport. I'm going."

I frowned. "Now?" I asked. "Without me?"

"I don't like surprises," he said, and his voice was firm. "I have reservations at the Dorchester. I've got meetings with publishers. I'm ready to gamble."

"So you're just going to leave me home?" I asked.

"No," he said. "You can come as soon as you get a new passport."

"Fine," I said, but my mind was already spinning. I heard a challenge and my honor was at stake. My mind was radar, scanning for a strategy. Mario thought I didn't really want to go, and I thought he was trying to escape without me so he could do whatever he wanted.

In that moment what became paramount was how I was going to foil his plan and trump him at his own game. Not a very loving thought, I must admit, but now I was obsessed. "After we drop you off, can I keep the limo?" I asked Mario. "I'll go right into the city, get a passport, and get back here before you know it."

"I don't think the passport office is open today," the limo driver told us from the front seat.

I sighed. "Let me ask the Concord big wigs," I said. "Maybe they can do something or get someone to make an exception."

Mario didn't say a word, and had a far away look in his eyes. He had already written me off. I could tell.

Once inside the airport, I ran up to the bigwigs lounge and asked to talk to the concierge. "Can you help me get a new passport right away?" I asked. I figured they must have some provisions in case an important person lost his or her passport. But the uniformed man behind the front desk—though he was very polite—just shook his head.

"Can't we call the embassy or the Pentagon or someplace?" I asked. "This is important. Mario Puzo is an important person and he has a cardiac problem so as a nurse I have to accompany him. It's a medical thing. An emergency."

Even to myself I sounded quite impassioned and sincere.

In contrast, Mario was sitting down in the lounge reading a newspaper as though nothing was happening.

I whispered to the concierge, "He can't be allowed to go alone. How will it look if there's a medical emergency and you hadn't helped me go with him?" I knew I was pushing it, but I am tenacious when there's a challenge and this was one.

Before I knew it, someone handed me a phone. Now, I was standing at the desk speaking to a young man from the Pentagon who told me, the passport office would only be open for one half hour more. After all, he informed me, it was Saturday morning, and the office closed at noon. I rattled off the emergency status of my request, reminded him that Mario was a National Treasure of sorts but he remained unmoved. He was impeccably polite as he told me that he would call ahead for me and let them know I was coming.

"Book me a seat on the next flight?" I asked the concierge as I raced past Mario, kissed him quickly, and tore through the lounge door, through the terminal and out the front door where the limo was waiting. Before the driver could get out to open my door, I jumped in.

"Take me to New York city, to the Passport office," I asked, breathless. "Please?"

There was a lot of traffic on the parkway and it seemed to take forever getting through the Midtown tunnel. Even worse, when we got into the city, the traffic was bumper to bumper.

"Come on..." I pleaded. "I've got to get back to the airport and I only have another hour."

The driver said, "There is nowhere to go. Traffic is stalled."

"No, no," I said. "I'm not complaining. I'm praying out loud."

"You will need two pictures," the driver explained. "There is a small photo shop on the corner. Go there first."

I kept looking at my watch. Mario was already in the sky by now, on his way to England.

Finally the traffic thinned and we stopped. "There," the limo driver said. "There's the photo shop." As I jumped out, he pointed down the block, "There's the Passport office."

Once inside the shop, I interrupted the couple at the counter and begged the guy behind, "Could you please take two passport photos? I have to catch a plane to England and I'm already late."

"Go, go," the older gentleman said. "Take the pictures."

"Thank you so much," I told him.

I tipped the ratty haired photographer and asked him to develop my pictures first, and convinced myself I wasn't being totally unethical under the circumstances. Then I automatically made the sign of the cross to ask for forgiveness knowing the meek would inherit the earth, but in that moment I didn't care. The guy who took my pictures had no such struggle. Within minutes I had my pictures.

I clutched them tight in my hand as I tore down the block to the Passport Office and ran up what seemed like a hundred steps with only two minutes to spare, completely out of breath. It was only because the uniformed guard at the door was good-natured that he let me slip through, just before he closed it for the day.

The woman behind the counter waited and then waved me forward toward the counter.

I babbled on about the Concord, and Mario and England and how my passport expired but she just looked at me, expressionless. She handed me an application and I quickly walked across the room to the counter scribbling while trying to fill it out.

"Two forms of ID please," was all she said, when I got back to the counter.

"I have a driver's license," I told her.

"Two forms," she said, without missing a beat.

"Credit cards are all I have," I said, feeling a little frantic.

She shook her head. "Birth certificate, social security card, utility bills, tax bill, something that proves who you are."

She looked at her watch. "We're closing soon."

"I know that," I told her. "But I have to catch a plane." I began to scout through my pocketbook to find something.

Finally when I had almost given up hope—at the very bottom of my pocketbook—I found an old hospital ID from the time I worked in the burn unit of a county hospital. This ID was complete with picture, fingerprints, name and anything else she could want. I showed it to her.

She looked at it and almost smiled.

Then without a word, she got me a passport, asked me to sign it, stamped it and said, "Hope you have a good flight." I think I caught a hint of a smile as I turned to run.

"Oh God," I said, "Thank you, thank you, thank you. Now if you wouldn't mind one more favor? Clear the parkway so we can get back to the airport quick!" My form of prayer.

The driver was waiting at the bottom of the stairs patiently pacing and looking like a fugitive because he was stopped in a no parking zone. When he saw me he raced over to open my door and I jumped right in. "How many minutes do we have?" I asked him.

"Eighteen," he answered simply.

"Oh God, can we make it?" I asked.

"With a lot of luck," he said.

"Okay," I said. "I think we're covered." I've always had great confidence in my prayers.

It seemed to take a very long time, though the traffic was lighter than usual, and we hit no roadblocks. I watched as the second hand on my watch hit every minute. With my stomach fluttering, we pulled into the airport and stopped in front of the Air France terminal. I yelled a thank you to the driver and tore through the terminal just in time. The gate was empty. The stewardess waved me on. I was the last one to board.

I flopped into the seat and took one deep breath and then another. I was on my way. Mario would be so surprised I made it. I myself was thrilled to death. I love a good challenge. I'd show him I could do what I had to do. I played the scene over and over and then suddenly a horrible thought hit me.

What if Mario thought I couldn't get there and so he thought he was free to do whatever he wanted? What if he had arrived and met someone else who he asked out to dinner? What if I arrived and he really didn't want me there? Oh God, too late to turn back.

I told myself to stop being a coward and face reality. I was a wreck. Still, that didn't stop me.

Within 3 hours, I was in England.

I got through customs in a minute and was in an old fashioned black London cab. I told the cabbie, "Dorchester Hotel, please?"

He turned and smiled. "Lovely day, isn't it ma'am?"

"It is," I said. I looked out the window at the people bustling down the streets shopping, talking and laughing. London cabbies are nothing like New York cab drivers. They drive like regular people so I wound up in front of the Dorchester in roughly the same condition I got into the cab. Amazing!

Once at the desk inside the Dorchester, I asked the concierge what room Mario was in. "I'll just ring him up and tell him you're on your way," he said cordially.

"Oh no," I said. Then spent the next ten minutes telling the poor man the whole tale of my misguided adventures. Finally I said, "I want to surprise him."

"Yes, Madame," he said. "I understand."

"Truly, I promise I'm supposed to be here," I told him. "I would never sneak up on someone to catch them doing something they weren't supposed to. I'm not that kind of person."

"Of course not, Madame," he said, leafing through the register. Then as he looked through the keys on the wall, he turned to me and whispered. "Suite 302. I wish you the best of luck, Madame."

My heart was pounding in my chest as I took the elevator up to the third floor. I didn't know how he would react, and hoped my being there wouldn't disappoint him.

In front of the door 302, I stood for a minute before I knocked. It had a "Do not disturb" sign hanging on the doorknob. If there's someone in there with him, I said to myself, I'll just fall down right here and he'll have to clean up the mess.

I hesitated for a moment before I knocked again.

Suddenly I heard the lock on the door click open. Mario opened the door slightly, leaving the chain intact. In that one moment, my eyes scanned his eyes, his clothes, and everything else as evidence of how he really felt. He was looking at me as though he didn't recognize me.

And he was dressed in a white ruffled tux shirt and dark pants. He hardly ever got dressed up.

"Carol?" he asked, in disbelief.

"Hi," I said. "I made it."

Mario blinked twice then dropped onto the floor laughing. Really laughing.

"Get off the floor, you lunatic," I said. "What's so funny?"

Tears were streaming down his face as he tried to speak. "Three hours. I only left you three hours ago. Without a passport, on a weekend, it still only took you three hours to catch me."

"It's that funny?" I asked.

When he stood up this time he kissed me on the nose and smoothed my hair. "It's funny," he said, "because I've always told everyone, 'if you're going to cheat, make sure you're at least 3000 miles away from home.' But now even 3000 miles isn't far enough." Then he laughed again.

"Jeez," I said. "You were going to cheat?"

"No," he said. "But now I know I can't even think about it."

"Why are you all dressed up?" I asked him then.

"I was going over to the casino," he explained. "Change your clothes and come with me."

The suite was elegant and very comfortable. The bed, couches and chairs were down filled and the bathtub was so big that if I didn't hang onto the sides, I would have slipped down under the water and drowned.

When I came out of the bathroom dressed to go, Mario was sitting in his chair reading, but he was still laughing. "I can't believe you got here in three hours," he repeated. "I underestimated you."

I had the best time gambling that night. So did Mario. Because I knew that he had really wanted me to come with him and he finally believed I wanted to be there.

Chapter 22

Mario had suffered night terrors his whole life. Especially when he was writing, then they got even worse. He woke up several times during each night, sweating and shaking. He'd get out of bed then, wash his face, brush his teeth and invariably cook something to eat to reorient himself.

Whenever Mario was writing a book, he tossed and turned and dreamed his scenes, in muted color with all the emotional betrayals, treacheries and dark deeds. Mario lived his Light but he wrote his Shadow. It was one of the things that made him even more reluctant to begin writing another book. He knew each time he put his felt tipped pen to paper, it meant months and years of night terrors until he finished it. He should have written comedies.

The one night I had a dream, it was a very strange one, unlike any I'd ever had before. It played out like a black and white movie complete with the menacing music of danger in the background. In one of the upstairs bedrooms at Mario's house, I saw a golden puma jumping through the air and suddenly falling to the floor—a puddle of bright red blood on the cream color carpeting.

I knew there was an inquiry because I saw several police officers dressed in black uniforms with badges shining light into the dark night. I knew Mario was a suspect in some crime.

At the front door, one of the officers was holding the leash of a German shepherd police dog, its leather collar biting into the long hair around his thick neck. The tag number read "57." The officer asked if he could come into the house.

The dog sniffed through Mario's house and then led the officer outside into Mario's yard. When I asked him what was going on, he explained that it had been reported that three men, "unsavory characters" was how he described them, had been playing cards in Mario's downstairs recreation room and they had been murdered. Now the police were looking for the bodies, but they were nowhere to be found. Obviously, under the circumstances, there had to be an investigation.

In the dream, the young officer led me back into the house, to Mario's game room, to show me an uneven stain of dark blood on the green carpet in front of the brick fireplace. The card table was still in place and four hands of cards lay on the felt table, face down. They had not yet been played.

"How do you know the men were killed?" I asked him.

He was a tall man with irregular features and dark skin. Without a word, he pointed to a heap of woolen overcoats that had been tossed on the carpet.

"Mario Puzo hit them with a hammer," the cop explained.

I nodded as though I understood. But a sudden alarm went off in my head. Something is wrong, I thought.

Then I saw Mario walking down the stairs from his upstairs bedroom. He was coming toward us. "What happened?" he asked me.

"Three men have been murdered," I told him but the policeman said nothing. The dog barked and the cop pulled him closer. "Their bodies are still missing."

Mario looked concerned.

There was a knock. "Get that honey?" Mario asked.

When I opened the front door, a tall African American detective showed me his badge and introduced himself. He walked past me into the living room, and as he passed I noticed the strong smell of too much cologne. I recognized that smell—Aramis.

Then as sometimes happens in dreams, there was another scene and Mario and I were standing in a courtroom, in front of a jury box, obviously on trial. Mario still looked terribly worried. He whispered, "But what did we do? I don't understand what we did?"

In the dream, I smiled a reassurance and explained. "Don't even worry about it. What can they do to us? Send us to the electric chair? So what? Then we'll be recycled, thrown back on the Rays and we'll be reborn and come back to life again. That jury is just a prop. It's like a staff of nurses and doctors. They can't really cure you. A person's healing has already been decided by Destiny. Only God can give breath. Only He can take it away."

Mario didn't find the same comfort in that concept that I did.

"But what did I do?" he asked again.

"They say you killed three men—with a hammer."

"I did no such thing," he protested, and I could see that his feelings were hurt.

"Oh," I said. "I know that. Really! I have no doubt."

The moment I woke up, I was so excited I wanted to tell Mario about the dream before I forgot it. "Mario," I said poking him, shaking him hard. "You wouldn't believe the dream I just had. It was so funny."

"Tell me," he said, still groggy.

But once I did, he sat straight up in bed and said, "That's not a dream, that's a nightmare!"

"Not for me," I said, laughing. "For me it was only a dream. For me there was no fear, so there was no nightmare."

Mario shook his head. Then he looked at me and said, "Well, I'm glad you knew I was innocent. How could you be so sure I didn't do it?"

"Because the cop said you killed them with a hammer," I explained, smiling. "That was the clue. You would never use a hammer," I said. "You would have used a dagger."

Mario jumped out of bed. "I would have preferred that you knew I could never do anything like that," he said. He walked toward his study. "You are a very strange girl."

"Ahh," I said, "But I thought that was a given."

Sometimes dreams are more than funny stories. They can also be foreshadowings.

Three weeks later, when we had both forgotten my dream....

It had been a great day. One of those days when we particularly enjoyed each other, or as Mario always said, we laughed a lot and didn't get on each others' nerves.

After I made dinner, we spent the evening working on and polishing another draft of one of Mario's screenplays for Godfather III in which Sonny and his girlfriend walked into his apartment after a date to find a group of thugs wearing black masks in his living room. One of the thugs grabbed the girlfriend, who was a tall blond, of course, and threatened Sonny with, "Give me the money or I'll cut her throat."

Mario leaned back thinking of the next scene and his eyes lit up as he dictated...

"Go on," Sonny said. Mario laughed.

"Why is that funny?" I asked him.

Mario kept laughing.

I said, "I don't think it's that funny."

He shook his head. "Nobody gets my sense of humor."

"Okay, I'll bite. Why is it funny to you?" I asked.

"Because it's not what you'd expect him to say," Mario said.

"Now, that's funny," I said. "Who expects a mafia guy to be sensitive?"

He frowned as he thought about it. Then he tried to explain. "You don't think of Sonny as a bad guy. He's young, warm blooded, but good hearted. He's a young knight. Sure, he was always a little hot headed, a little reckless, but he lived by a code of honor. He was soft hearted with women. In this case, she was a damsel in distress."

"Are we talking about King Arthur here," I asked. "Or the Godfather?"

"Same thing," he said. And we dropped the conversation.

That night Mario fell asleep before I did, and I sat up in bed watching TV. But my head was doing funny tricks. I noticed that the actors in the movie I was watching seemed particularly stiff and spoke with click-clack tongues of wood. By the time I shut the TV, I was whipped and fell asleep quickly.

It was about 4 in the morning when I felt a tap on my shoulder which woke me up. But Mario was still fast asleep. I tried to stay in bed for a few minutes, but then decided to go to the bathroom.

I had to pass the door to Mario's study on the way. There, standing in the open doorway, I saw a very tall man dressed in dark clothes wearing a black ski mask. Only the whites of his eyes showed.

I stopped and looked at him. Puzzled.

For months now, I had been studying the life of the Buddha for a course in Transpersonal Psychology. In my research, I had been particularly taken by the concept of Kama Mara. I knew that before the Buddha could reach enlightenment, he had to sit unmoving under a Bodhi tree and watch as both The Faces of Death and The Faces of Desire danced before him. If he could stay perfectly still, he could break through Illusion, see Truth, and reach Enlightenment.

On that night, the story of the Buddha, the story of the Godfather, and the story of King Arthur were floating around in my brain.

So it was with that crazy mix of thoughts, that I laughed when I saw the tall masked burglar standing in the doorway of Mario's study. I couldn't figure out whether this was my Buddhist test of Truth or Illusion to reach enlightenment in contemporary times or Sonny and the Grade B thug left over from the scene Mario and I had been working on the evening before.

Buddhists believe that thought makes form, I reminded myself. So, I stood fast. If the Buddha could sit tight, so could I. Enlightenment? Again, I laughed aloud.

Then I saw the Tai Chi circle around him. A half circle of light. Somehow, I knew not to step into it. I scanned his body slowly and my eyes went from his feet upward until I saw his black gloved hand. In it he held a long black flashlight. Some kind of moving energy seemed to be swirling around his left ankle which caught my attention. Everything seemed to be a still shot rather than a moving picture. When my eyes met his, I stopped and tried to look closely. I had the mad desire to giggle again, to ask him, *"What the heck are you doing in that getup?"* He felt so familiar to me. But before I could say a word, he suddenly bowed and backed away into Mario's study and closed the door.

That's when I panicked. "Good God," I thought. "There are no closed doors on the path of enlightenment. This must be the last scene from The Godfather, and I'm in the wrong movie!"

I called to Mario. "Mario, wake up," said. "I think there's a burglar in your study."

He jumped out of bed and ran over to the door holding tight to the doorknob. "Are you sure?" he asked.

"Not at all," I said. "It could be a dream."

"Call the police," he told me.

"But what if I'm wrong?" I asked.

"Go downstairs and get a knife," he ordered.

"You think that's a good idea?" I said, shaking my head and thinking, he would never suggest that if he had seen how big that guy was. Still, I opened the door to the bedroom and walked down the stairs into the kitchen. Once there, I pulled open one of the cutlery drawers and pulled out two large carving knives. Then I ran quickly upstairs and back into the bedroom.

Mario was still holding tight to the doorknob. "Mario, you better get some pants on if I'm going to call the police," I said.

He held his hand out and I gave him one of the knives.

When he saw that I held another, he began to laugh. "You brought two?" he asked, incredulously.

"Of course," I said. "If they skewer you, do you think I want to be defenseless?"

"Call the cops," he said, still laughing. Then he slowly opened the door.

Neither of us expected what we saw.

The glass doors to the study were wide open and a cold breeze was blowing in. The room had been completely ransacked and was strewn with papers. My pocketbook, the one that had been on the floor right next to my side of the bed, was on the couch, thrown open and my wallet had been emptied. My telephone book and all my ID's including my license were still there on the couch. The back of Mario's desk had been pulled away from the wall and several of the drawers were opened and had been rummaged through.

I went back into the bedroom and picked up the phone. When the 911 operator answered I told her, "Better send the police over, this is Mario Puzo's house. We've been robbed."

Then, I looked over to where we had placed Mario's suitcase the night before, and that too was missing.

That's when Mario remembered my dream...

It took more than 6 months for the police to track the burglar down, and during that 6 months my mind tracked him as well. He had stolen my Louis Vuitton carry on bag when he left and so my consciousness or some part of me was still able to follow him during that time. He was accused of burglary and rape. Many charges, many victims—on Long Island, Staten Island and Florida. During that time, I had more terrible dreams than I can remember.

When Mario and I were finally called to testify before the Grand Jury for the burglar's indictment, I told the story just as I told it here. The prosecutor was less than amused. Still, there were 14 others who had been raped—young girls—some taken from their rooms in the homes of their families. Many more who had been robbed. They wanted justice. By then they had dubbed him the "South Shore rapist," and their families needed some peace. I didn't want to add to my karmic debt, so I would have preferred not to testify, but Mario insisted we do our part and tell the truth. So, I did.

Before the trial, I didn't know how I could possibly identify a man whose face I had not truly seen because of a mask. But at the trial, there was no mistaking him. I took one look at him sitting at the table, writing furious notes on a long legal pad, and I knew. How? I just felt I knew him, and all I could think of is, *what are you doing in a place like this?* I wanted to laugh. That's what gave it away. It wasn't a nervous laugh. I wasn't afraid, it just seemed absurd to me. I didn't really get it. But I did know it was him. The man in Mario's study.

His smart ass attorney asked if I often saw things that weren't there, and I said, "You asked for my truth, I gave it to you."

Then, when Mario was on the stand, his attorney asked, "Did you find a horse's head in your bed?"

I thought he should never have been the defense attorney. He should have been the prosecuting attorney.

But the jury got it right. The South Shore rapist was accused of 322 counts of burglary and rape.

That night, I had another dream. This time I heard it, saw nothing. Just this: "Heavenly justice has been accomplished. This man finally knows his soul purpose. He will not see freedom for a long long time."

He was not declared guilty on the charges of robbing Mario's house. No karmic debt. But still, it was my Louis Vuitton bag he had tried to sell, because I recognized the large red felt magic marker stain on the bottom of it. That pen had broken in Vegas during one of our trips when I was helping Mario edit one of his books.

Still, Justice was served. The South Shore burglar received a sentence of 322 years. He won't see freedom for a very long time. Truth.

Chapter 23

The Hamptons on the east end of Long Island is a beautiful place—truly Nature's Landscape. It's not only several small towns dotted with beautiful people. It has both farms and mansions and each of the towns in the Hamptons has a very different atmosphere. Some have the best of small town living and others' have a cultural advantage, a town filled with the artists; writers, as well as actors and musicians and famous chefs who served great cuisine.

East Hampton is a writer's community. Lots of writers had summer houses out there before it was discovered by the rich and famous as a summer playground.

Mario's friend, Joe Heller, best known for his book Catch 22, had a house in East Hampton and we often went to visit before we eventually bought a house of our own. Because it's about a 2 hour drive and in the summer the traffic is horrendous, sometimes we'd stay overnight at Joe's guest house so Mario could catch up with some of his other friends while we were out on the east end of Long Island.

Mario had other famous friends as well but most of his old friends came from the Bronx or NY rather than Hollywood. Joe Stein, whose Fiddler on the Roof and Zorba were two of my favorite musicals on Broadway. There was Mel Brooks who was famous for Blazing Saddles which made me cringe, and The Elephant Man which I loved, plus The Producers. His wife, the actress Anne Bancroft, was a personal favorite of mine, especially for her part in the Miracle Worker which helped fuel my desire to be a healer from the time I was young. Bruce Friedman also lived out there, and Mario often told stories of how they'd worked together on Male magazines where Bruce gave him a shot writing under a pseud-onym. Those were his fun days writing to feed his family. That's where he met his friend, Ivan Prasker who he had special affection for. He was always grateful to Bruce for helping him save face by giving him a job—even if it was a hack job, as he put it.

Our weekends in the Hamptons were fun because after a while I knew most of his friends and I got to hang out with them. There, we could go to the Palm Restaurant; eat a five pound lobster and great steaks. Better put, *I* got to eat a huge lobster cause Mario hat-ed even the look of anything with claws. I used to tease him merci-lessly and after a while unless I promised only to order food that didn't look as though it could fight back, Mario said he'd prefer not to sit next to me at the table.

On this particular weekend, everyone in the Hampton's was going to a big dinner at Craig Claiborne's house. He was the fa-mous New York Times Food Critic and every year he hosted a huge dinner party. It was supposed to be such a big deal that even the socialites from New York came out to the Island to attend. But nei-ther Mario or I liked those kinds of gatherings, so we were going to eat at Joe's house and keep him company because he was still re-covering from his Guillain-Barre Syndrome. He wasn't completely comfortable because he wasn't yet steady on his feet.

There were only six of us for lunch that day. Joe and his wife Valerie, Speed and his wife Lou Ann, Me and Mario. It was a beau-tiful day and the ride out there wasn't bad which was great for me because I was driving.

By the time we got there the table was already tastefully set, and it looked like it was going to be the beginning of a really fun kind of day. But then as we all were sitting around the table, catching up on our books, our travels, our family and friends, Mario began to eat. First he chose some of the antipasto, then a roll, then some cheese. He chose one thing after another, and I was watching him like a hawk because his diabetes was getting really hard to control.

In fact, it was only a couple of months before that he had snuck away from me in Vegas while we were shopping, drank a large chocolate shake and ate a donut, and promptly fell unconscious for the next two days.

I sat in the suite at the Sands, worried to death, not knowing whether to call the kids or not, not being able to rouse him. Two days of watching TV, eating room service, and taking his blood pressure and testing his blood sugar. By the time he opened his eyes, and was conscious, I was a crazy person. His blood sugar was over 300 while the normal is 80 to 120.

"What the hell happened," I asked him. "What did you eat? Or drink?"

"One lousy malted," was all he said. Then he added, "And one lousy donut."

"I can't believe you did that," I said. "You know it's no good for you? Even your doctor warned you."

He sat up and smiled. "Why did you let me?" he asked.

"This is not going to happen again," I swore. "If you're going to eat or drink yourself into a coma, it's going to be on someone else's watch."

"Thank you, honey," he said.

That day I really wanted to kill him myself.

Now, at the table at Joe's house, that scene kept playing through my mind. I touched Mario's arm a couple of times as he reached for food. He didn't seem to notice. But Joe did.

The next time he reached for a roll, I said, "Mario, don't."

When dessert came, Mario took a large piece of chocolate cake, so I said, "Mario, don't."

Joe looked at Mario and said, "You going let her stop you?"

"Don't," I said to Joe. "He'll get sick."

Mario looked at both of us, but said nothing. Then he reached for another roll.

"Mario, no more," I said.

Joe looked at me. "Leave him alone. You're not his mother," he said.

I looked at Mario, then I looked at Joe. "Joe," I said. "Everyone keeps telling me you're so much more. I still haven't seen it."

When I got up, Mario got up too and followed me to the door. "I won't eat with that man," I told Mario. As I stormed out the door,

I said to Mario, "Why didn't you stick up for me? You know what's going on..."

Mario just looked at me. "He's a cripple," he said, softly. Then he stopped, took a deep breath, and added, "A pox on both your houses!"

I stormed out to the cottage determined to pack my suitcase and leave. But right behind me, I could see Joe with his cane hobbling across the lawn toward the cottage.

I took my overnight case and was just about to put it on the bed, when Joe came in and sat down at the foot of the bed.

"Carol..." Was all he got to say, before I launched into a tirade. "Joe," I said. "I don't get it. What the hell are you doing? You know how sick he gets. What do you do in your spare time, beat up old ladies in dark alleys, or just pull the legs off spiders? I know you're afraid of being rejected—it doesn't take a genius to see that—but then you set yourself up by forcing people to reject you. Well, not me. I mean you have no fight with me. I won't put myself through this. I know you're smart, why don't you use your damn brains for good instead of tormenting people..." and on and on I went as I paced in front of him. I held nothing back.

In all the years Mario and I had been together, I had never yelled at Mario the way I yelled at Joe that day, I had never spoken to Mario like that. But of course, he hadn't deserved it. I was still livid, still pacing, as I looked out the window and saw everyone else walking toward the cottage from the house.

It was Speed who opened the door, and asked softly, "Everyone alright in here?"

I looked at Joe. Joe looked at me.

Then Joe turned to Speed and said, "Everything's fine. She apologized."

Chapter 24

Mario and I had been together for quite some time when one night after a really good day of working on his latest book, we were lying in bed, and Mario asked, "You don't really like sex do you?"

I frowned. "I do," I said. "I think it's fun."

"Has it ever been more fun, or something more than fun for you?"

"You're asking me if any other guys have been better in bed?" I asked.

Mario laughed. "We're not kids," he said, "so you can tell me the truth."

"You told me you never want the truth," I said laughing.

"But in this case, I want to know. I want to know how women feel about things."

"I love pizza," I said, smiling. "But I wouldn't eat it 3 times a day five days a week."

Mario was quiet. "Too much?" he asked.

"Look Mario," I said, sitting up and leaning back against the headboard. "You have large appetites. I like that. I love your enthusiasm. You eat more than I do, you gamble with wild abandon, you have more fun."

"What are you saying?" he asked.

"I'm saying that there's never been a man with better technique or equipment long enough to touch my soul."

I just shook my head. I knew I was missing something about the whole sex thing, but no matter how hard I tried, I couldn't understand how it sucked everyone in. I mean I spent years when I was young reading everything there was to read about technique, about lovemaking, about what to do and what not to do. I loved mastery so I learned it well. But still, I didn't really get its allure.

Some of the smartest women I knew—once they fell into bed with a man—seemed to be crippled by the power of the connection. They truly seemed to lose their minds. If the sex was good, they were sunk, they would give up everything for that man. If the sex was bad, even a good man couldn't keep them.

"So, you like sex, but just not that much?" he asked. "You're a good Catholic girl. Religion has ruined more women than anything else."

"Wrong," I said. "That's not it. I just don't get it. It can even feel good for a short time, but that's it."

"That's not enough?" he asked.

"It's fine," I said. "It's just not more than other important parts of any relationship."

"You know what men really want from women?" Mario asked. By now he was sitting up too. He reached over and took a cigar off his nightstand, put it in his mouth, but didn't light it.

"Nope," I said. "Surrender probably. Power mostly."

Mario looked surprised. "It's the one place I don't play for power," he said. "I know there are some guys like that, the kind of a guy who sleeps with a girl and brags about it. But that guy is a creep in other ways. It doesn't work that way for me."

I laughed. "That's how it used to work for me," I said. "I was like one of those guys who scratches a notch in his rifle each time he kills a bear. I mean that's how it was for me. Not now. Now I'm over it. I like you too much."

When he looked puzzled I said, "I mean I don't mind sleeping with a guy if he's lonely, or scared, as a kindness. It's just not a passion for me. Mostly I'm willing to do it *for* someone, not for *me*. I just found out that once you can get a guy out of his clothes, he'll talk. I mean not the trivial bullshit kind of talk, but really talk."

He looked over at me and smiled. "You're a funny little thing," he said. "In your whole life, you never met anyone you felt passionate about?"

"I didn't say that," I told him. "I said I don't feel passionate about a guy when I'm sleeping with him. Sex isn't what makes me feel close. In fact, it pushes me right back into myself. That's not how I connect."

Mario reached over and tousled my hair. "You should tell your body that," he said. "Were you pretending?"

I made a face. "I don't do that. Early on I might have, but not once I grew up and figured out that pretending robbed me of something special and didn't give my partner a chance."

Mario and I sat quietly thinking for a long time. Then he reached over and held my hand. "I think sex is more of a spiritual thing for guys," he said. "It's the way they connect to the world, through a woman. It makes them feel safe, and accepted. Not completely alone."

"I know that," I told him. "I also know that while that's going on, it pushes the fear of death away. But women connect in other ways. They know they can have kids, that they and another can be so connected that if one of them dies the other does too. Even women who don't have children know there's that connection. It's not as abstract as it is with men."

"Is there anything that makes it better for you?" Mario asked me.

"You mean like foreplay?" I asked, and I laughed.

"*Nothing*?" he asked again.

"My idea of foreplay is deep and meaningful conversation," I said. "If you like pizza and want me to eat 3 pizzas a day, talk to me an hour for each, and it's my pleasure. If you want pizza five times a week, talk to me an hour five times a week. I'm easy."

Mario laughed. "Makes sense," he said. "You know what else men really want from a woman?"

"Not really," I said. "Tell me. What?"

"The first time a man drops his trousers, he wants a woman to gasp with wonder and amazement. But he also wants to know that if any other man drops his trousers, that very same woman would instantly throw up."

I laughed. "Can't promise either," I said. "Too many years of nursing. What I can promise is that I like you enough that I'll eat all the pizza you want, as long as you talk to me."

"Deal," Mario said. "Makes sense."

"Does that upset you?" I asked. "To know how I really feel? Are you going to feel rejected now and am I going to have to start pretending?"

He looked at me and spoke gently when he said, "I want you to be yourself. I'm not one of those pain in the ass guys who insists others enjoy what they do. If I want pizza, and you're willing to come with me, I'm grateful. Thank you."

"Conversation?" I said.

"Okay," he agreed. "But as long as we're telling each other the truth, I don't like talking any more than you like pizza."

"I didn't say I didn't like it," I said, again. "Neither pizza or sex. I said it's not the way I connect most. It's not what makes me feel intimate with another."

"That's what I just said," he said. "So, we're good now, right?"

Before we went to sleep that night, in the dark, I asked, "Are you disappointed with me?"

He spoke softly, "No. I'm glad you told me how you feel. I know you wish I would talk more."

"I mean I can sleep with a stranger, but I can't make love to a stranger," I said.

"Understood," he said. "You don't care if I sleep with someone, as long as I don't talk to them."

"Don't tease me," I said. "That's not fair."

"Couldn't help myself," he said. "You're such an easy mark."

Chapter 25

When Mario and I first started traveling together, I wanted to see everything in the world and travel everywhere. But after a few years of going to Vegas, Malibu, Cannes, and London several times and spending most of our time in gambling casinos or with movie people, I began to moan and groan about it.

I was shy and self-conscious which few people who knew me would believe because I was talkative and appeared extroverted, but I swear it was pure nerves. Meeting so many new people threw me into a real panic. Not in the wards of hospitals where I had passion and purpose but on any other ordinary street corner. Though I was young and good looking enough not to hurt anyone's eyes, I still didn't like dressing up. I didn't have a flair for it. Each time I had to go somewhere I tried on so many outfits they were strewn all over my bed and floor before I could even find one that looked right. Thank God for my sister, Bibs, and on the West Coast, Lanetta, who bought my clothes and dressed me when I couldn't bear to do it.

Even more than my own self-consciousness was the awesome responsibility I felt for keeping Mario safe.

By the time I met him, Mario had already had one heart attack and his diabetes was completely out of control. He wasn't on any kind of medication because he was supposed to control his "sugar" with diet. Diet? Every time I mentioned it to Mario, he acted as though I was speaking in a foreign tongue. Whether we were in Vegas, or Cannes, or England, or Malibu, Mario loved to try all kinds of local food and I lived on a blade of terror. Because unlike my father, whose motto in life was "Everything in moderation," Mario's was "Everything in excess."

I loved that about him. His passionate appetites and obsessive excesses.

Mario was a big thinker but he wasn't a big talker-except when he was working on a book and wanted to discuss an idea or a character with me and so I spent a lot of time when we were away from home, alone.

Now, I'd be lying if I said it's not my nature to haunt. It's one of the things I do best. Especially when I feel responsible for someone. Both my kids and Mario's too would attest to that, and it's always been a pain in the ass for all of us no matter how well intentioned I am. For me, taking responsibility for someone I really care about takes a lot of energy.

The night I found out that my best friend Frany had a particularly aggressive form of breast cancer, I ran over to Mario's house to fall apart.

Frany was born in England and had come to America as a nanny when she was young. We had been together for so long, I could never even remember how we'd met. She lived in the house next to my parents when I was a kid, and now she lived with me and my kids. She was staid and logical and had always been there to shore up my life.

During dinner, I told him. He seemed saddened. Mario liked Frany—for one thing he liked tall blonds, another, she spoke with an English accent and he loved everything English.

"How is she taking it?" he asked.

"She's sad that she hasn't lived life fully enough," I told him. "I think she would have liked to see more of the world."

"Want to ask her to go with us to Venice?" he asked.

"Good God," I said, touched. "What have you become? A 'Make a Wish' kind of guy?"

Later, upstairs in Mario's study, we sat on the couch together listening to opera music by Andrea Bocelli. We were both thinking, not doing much talking. A few high notes of the opera La Boehme played in the background. "I usually hate concerts," I said. "But if I ever considered going to any, he's the man I'd love to see in person."

"I didn't know you liked concerts," he said.

"I don't," I said. "But I admire him. I figure if he can whip up the courage to walk on stage without being afraid of falling into the orchestra pit even though he's blind, I too can do anything. He inspires me."

Mario reached over and put his arm around my shoulders. "Okay," he said, "If he comes to town, and there's any way I can do it, I'll take you to a concert of his."

"Really?" I said, surprised.

"I'll make sure you get to see him in person," he said, waving his hand playfully. "I'm a magician remember."

Later the following day I was sitting in my living room drinking tea and talking to Frany. "Mario wants to take me to Cannes this year," I told her. "Then he wants to go to Nice, Florence and Venice. As usual, I moaned and groaned. But Mario said it would help me be a better writer."

"Oh, Carol," Frany said, laughing, "You're so crazy. How can you make it seem like you're doing Mario a favor by letting him take you to some of the most beautiful places on earth?"

"Everyone knows I'm a hermit," I said, "but nobody seems to get how frantic it makes me to leave my kids, my house and my stuff."

"What stuff?" she said.

"All my research, my books, my friends, the place I feel safe," I explained.

"He didn't invite you on an African safari," she said. "Though that too would have been lovely. He's offering to take you to places that are the origins of civilization, hubs of cultural diversity, and you're not exactly having to rough it by camping out. You'll be staying in four or five star hotels not washing your clothes at the river bank."

"I know that," I said, "But now you're being reasonable, and my emotions aren't reasonable. The truth is that I'd rather travel with Mario than anybody. But running around having fun doesn't seem to be one of my strengths."

"There must be something you can learn from it," she said, smiling, "or something you can do to give a marvelous trip some practical value."

I sat thinking about it. "Well," I said, "I know I'm doing something necessary when I can stop Mario from destroying himself, and I can even have some fun then. I do love the glitzy glamour of the casinos and I love watching Mario gamble. He does it with such single-minded focus and passion that it's almost a religious experience. It's a Zen exercise of living in the moment—and being totally present. Besides, it strikes me that in this culture it is one of the few ways a man can practice his intuition. But when he eats too much and gets sick, I feel awful and responsible besides."

Frany asked. "So that's the reason you think you are willing to go?"

I thought about it. "Not only." I said, "To be completely honest if I don't go, he could ask someone else. Truth is I love shopping with him because he's even more excessive than I am—but still basically I'm a hermit." I stopped, took a sip of tea, and added, "All I'm doing is sharing my conflict. I realize I'm not going to get a lot of sympathy from my friends especially you—who is now facing a life-threatening illness—by complaining about having to go to the Riviera and Venice. I mean I get how ridiculous I sound."

"One thing has nothing to do with another. I think it's wonderful," Frany said, "If Mario didn't drag you out of the house you'd probably live and die on Long Island. Now that would be dreadful." Her face was tan and she looked particularly young and healthy, though I was wary of the rosy blush of her cheeks. "Someday I'll see those places too. I've always dreamed about them. Especially Venice," she said, "I'm just hoping I don't run out of time."

"How about coming with us?" I asked her.

"Venice is the City of Lovers," she added, "Mario wouldn't want me along."

"He was the one who suggested it," I told her. "He thinks we'd all have more fun if you came. That way we could shop and talk to each other and he could spend as much time as he wanted to in the hotel room, reading. Besides, in case he feels like coming out, he likes your company."

Frany's eyes lit up, but it was several minutes before she could speak. "I can finally ride in a gondola," she said. "And see the Bridge of Sighs."

"Is that a 'yes?'" I asked. "You'd be willing to close down your floral design shop for a week or so? You can meet us in Nice after the film festival."

"That's a yes," she said and hugged me.

"Sounds great," I said, "You and I can sightsee a little and I'll feel like a foreign exchange student which will give more meaning to my 'fun.' The only thing Mario wants to do is visit the art museums so he can do more research on the Borgia and Medici families. He wants to write a book about the church and the Popes. He thinks they were the original crime families. The Popes—the greatest Dons of all."

Frany threw her head back and laughed. "No matter what happens after this, I can say I lived my life fully."

Three weeks later Mario and I took the Concord and flew to Paris. Then we took a small plane to Nice. There, the airport was buzzing with the sounds and frantic excitement of those who had come to be a part of the Cannes film festival.

I was stunned as we drove from the airport into Nice itself. It was as though the world had suddenly been transformed from black and white to color. The clear azure sky formed a perfect backdrop for the rolling hills and mountains, so green and manicured that they could have come from a needlepoint tapestry.

Once in Nice, stately palm trees lined the wide boardwalk called the Promenade Des Anglais. Richly colored yellow, red and pink flowers in full bloom surrounded the pastel palaces along the sidewalks to my right but to the left, the gentle waves from the Baie des Anges spilled onto sandy white beaches.

That year because Cannes was always so crowded, Mario made reservations for us at the Negresco Hotel, in Nice. Nice was less than 20 miles away from Cannes and less frenetic. The Negresco was an exquisite white stucco palace with tall pink and turquoise turrets straight out of the Arabian Nights.

As soon as our car pulled up, a bellman opened the door, while another carried our luggage into the front lobby where several more bellmen appeared.

At the hotel, two well-built young doormen dressed in stylish ruby jackets with epaulets, and golden buttons over black knickers stood guarding the entrance. The velvet top hats made both men look tall as they stood on each side of the giant glass and gold doors.

The check in was only a nod between Mario and the concierge before he led us toward a deeply carved mahogany door that one of the bellman held open for us.

The elevator—no larger than a Telephone booth—with tufted walls of red velvet was barely big enough to hold the three of us. Mario and I were standing shoulder-to-shoulder at first, and later nose-to-nose, until we reached the third floor where the door was opened by another royally dressed bellman.

The concierge led us into the bedroom of a luxurious suite. The walls were covered with gold medallion flocking on red silk. I had never seen silk wallpaper before and it tickled me. The double bed was a shiny carved mahogany swan partially hidden beneath a red silk canopy, its drapes pulled to the bedposts with thick twisted satin ropes. Two small alabaster tables stood alongside the bed, one with a gold and crystal standing lamp on it. I felt as though I had just walked into a fairy tale.

The concierge was very serious when he announced, "This was the bed of Napoleon and Josephine."

"It's pretty small," I said aloud.

With no hint of a smile, the concierge, said, "In those times, we were not a very large people."

I laughed. "Perfect for us," I said to Mario. He was no more than 5'7" and I was inches shorter.

"Napoleon was a great strategist," Mario explained. "I want to write a story about him too. The time period fascinates me, and so does European history, but even more, I like the idea of the love story. Except it probably won't sell."

"I'd read it," I told him. "I don't know anything about history so it would all be new to me. I went to Catholic school so I only heard the glory parts not the seedy stuff."

"Poor girl," Mario said, walking behind me.

We followed the concierge through the bedroom along the leopard skin carpeting into the light and airy living room. I pointed to the carpeting. "Mario," I said, "This is so over the top I can't believe it. How could they live with this?"

"I like it," he said.

"I'm not classy enough," I told him. "It's so gaudy, it makes me laugh. I guess I don't appreciate it in the same way."

This room, decorated in white and green velvet was furnished with Louis the XIV antiques. All the chairs and dressers had been restored and in each corner of the large living room there stood a green Dieffenbachia plant.

The concierge pulled open golden drapes to step out onto the balcony so we could see the Mediterranean.

In the lemon colored afternoon sun, a stately yacht led three small boats like ducklings across the clear blue water. Beautiful men and women—topless and tan—dotted the white sandy beach in front of us while French flags flew in celebration of an upcoming festival.

Mario put his arm around my shoulders. "Take a good look at this, kiddo," he said, "This is as good as it gets."

I looked at him with mock horror. "This is as good as it gets?"

He swatted me affectionately.

"Frany will think she died already when she sees this," I said to him.

"I hope not," he answered seriously. "I hope she has a wonderful time."

"Come on, Mario," I said, "Don't act like death is the end of the world."

"Some day I'm going to strangle you," he said teasingly. "You and your life after death theories."

"Heaven, Mario, is what I mean," I said, but then I remembered he didn't believe in heaven either.

Carol surrounded by "The Nurse's Story" manuscript 1980

Mario on the balcony in Cannes 1981

David Marks, Carol and Mario in Cannes 1981

Mario in Montelepre, Palermo, Sicily. Native city of the Sicilian bandit, Salvatore Guiliano 1982

Necropoli di Montelepre (Palermo) "Fummo come voi...sarete come noi." We were once like you. You will be like us. 1982

Carol, Mario and Frany in Venice 1985

Carol, Mario and Frany on the boat in Venice 1985

At the Gritti Palace in Venice. Hemingway Suite 1985

Carol and Mario at a book signing for "The Sicilian" 1985

Mario autographing books

Mario karate chop

Christmas

Carol during "Rusty's Story" book tour 1986

At Burgess Meredith's House in Malibu 1989

Dashing Mario

Carol and Mario

Mario "Brando" 1996

Chapter 26

The next three weeks passed quickly and before I knew it, it was early morning and Mario and I were standing at the gate in Nice Airport waiting for Frany's plane to arrive.

As soon as I saw her disembark, I stopped worrying about her. She was wearing a bright red blouse and had tied a red scarf around her blond hair. She was walking toward us at the speed of light.

"It was the most wonderful flight," she exclaimed happily. "I feasted on champagne and filet mignon and chocolate covered pralines."

"Consider yourself a jet setter," I said, laughing. "For seven days. Not a lot of time to see the world."

"I know but still, it's more than I ever imagined," she said.

Mario asked her, "Would you like to spend the afternoon gambling in Monte Carlo?"

"Oh," she said excitedly, "I'd love to."

"We can get a limo to drive us up the coast to Monte Carlo by lunch time," he said, "Then we can gamble for a few hours and drive on to Florence by nightfall."

"You'd rather go gambling in Monte Carlo then shopping in Nice?" I asked Frany.

"I'd rather do it all," she said.

"Well," Mario said, "if we can get to Florence tonight we can spend two full days there and still have two or three days in Venice."

"Sounds great to me," I said.

"Me too," Frany said. "I can shop anywhere."

Back at the Negresco, when Frany saw the suite, she was speechless. She slowly walked through the rooms and lovingly ran her hands over the marble topped tables and across the shiny veneer of the wooden dressers. Then she walked over to the terrace and stood looking out.

It was always such a shock to me that in the midst of my greatest tragedies—and the possibility of my best friend Frany dying was one of them—the world still spun on its axis as it always had. While my inner world had shattered into a million pieces, the outer world stayed intact. But now, as I looked at Frany and she smiled, I understood that she was very different from me. She was comforted by the constancy of nature and by its beauty. The very 'intactness' that disturbed me was the thing that made her feel secure.

"Would you like breakfast on the terrace?" Mario asked and both of us nodded.

As the waiter dressed in his starched white jacket wheeled in our breakfast on a cart covered with a damask tablecloth and folded pink damask napkins, I watched Frany's wide eyed expression.

Mario was already on the terrace behind his newspaper. He lowered the paper and asked, "What have we got?"

There were fragrant flaky croissants and soft rolls in silver baskets alongside small butter dishes and jelly jars. White ceramic tea pots, steaming hot, stood alongside shorter glass coffee carafes. Several individual pitchers were filled with cream so thick and yellow that it looked like melted butter.

"On the balcony, Monsieur?" the waiter asked.

"Merci..." Mario answered. I thought it was pretty funny that the waiter was talking in English and Mario was answering in French.

After breakfast with all our luggage packed in the trunk of the dark blue Mercedes limo, Mario, Frany and I left for Monte Carlo.

Monaco is a tiny country, only about two miles long with the Mediterranean Sea on one side and the Maritime Alps on the other. Riding through the middle of it to Monte Carlo, there seemed to be no other place as beautiful. Everything for miles around seemed white and gold. In the center of town, expensively dressed people, tan and laughing, walked to new and shiny cars. Bright colorful flowers, different from any I'd ever seen, decorated the sidewalks. Small parks, filled with large shade trees, were placed like green oases amidst the immaculate white concrete.

Around a center island covered with a carpet of green and filled with more brightly colored flowers, there stood several large pillared buildings. They looked austere, like government buildings to me. In front of the largest one, flags flew from high poles while guards in full regalia stood tall and stiff. There was dignity and order.

"The casino. Monsieur," the driver told us as we pulled in front.

That building looked more like a cathedral than a courtroom to me. Sacrosanct. I felt like I did in Church as a little kid, as though I should whisper as we walked up the stairs and through the large stained-glass front doors. Even Frany was quiet. Inside, behind a large dark wooden desk, two men dressed in black tuxedos smiled slightly and asked to see our passports.

But once we were inside the glass doors to the main rooms, there were slot machines with fluorescent pink, blue and yellow flashing neon lights in long rows lining each of the walls. I laughed out loud. It was in such contrast to the graceful exterior. This room could have been Vegas.

Men and women dressed in casual summer clothes sat smoking cigarettes and clicking ice cubes in tall drinks while never taking their eyes off the one-armed bandits.

Mario led us through two more rooms until there was another gentleman who greeted us. "Monsieur, please go right in."

The massive wooden doors with thick black iron handles led into a private room. Stepping across that threshold was like stepping into another world completely. The room was enormous and lit by several ornate crystal chandeliers. Thick burgundy velvet drapes with tassels and roping covered the long French windows as we walked across the room to the cashier's cage.

Mario bought us chips to gamble while I looked around. There were about eight roulette tables. At each, the tuxedo dressed croupier sat on a high bar stool behind a curved glass windshield while another croupier sat at the head of the table, and one more was stationed at the foot. Surrounding the tables stood several very sedate, well-dressed men and women. In front of each was a shiny stack of colorful plastic chips. The croupier's eyes darted from one player to another as each of the players put down their chips. There were thirty-six numbers on the green felt board.

Roulette was my favorite kind of gambling. I loved to watch Mario play. When he got hot and his numbers began to come up, he again went into a trance. He didn't see or hear anything outside himself then. He gave up all reason and focused on some inner voice of the gods who were speaking to him. Past thought, past intellect, he placed his chips on his numbers with both passion and confidence.

Of course, when he lost he took it quite personally. Then he could no longer trust himself or his universe. Then it was not fun. Mario got sullen, spoke even less than usual and got depressed. During those times, nothing was right: Until the gods spoke again and he won or we had managed to flee the casinos and as he put it, were where "we couldn't get hurt." It was the closest thing to religion Mario practiced.

Mario handed Frany and I each a stack of red twenty franc chips. For himself he played 500-franc gold chips.

"How much is each of these?" Frany whispered, holding up the ruby chip.

"About five dollars," Mario explained.

When Frany gasped, Mario told her, "Just go bet and get lucky."

"Each time I place one of the chips on a number," Frany said, "It means I'm betting five dollars? On one number?"

"You can put it on the line between two numbers," Mario instructed. "That's called a split."

When we reached the table, I put down about four chips on my regular numbers. Three, six, nine, and twelve but Frany only put down one.

"There's a Minimum." the croupier reprimanded Frany by pointing at the sign with his long rake. That stick was used to rake all the losing chips off the board. Now it was leaning on a small sign which instructed "Minimum—100 francs." I put down another chip but Frany hesitated.

"That's twenty-five dollars on the spin of a wheel," she whispered horrified, when I looked at her with a puzzled expression.

"You've gambled bigger stakes," I reminded.

"Will..." she whispered slowly as she reached across the table and placed her bets. "I'll just will my numbers to come up. "

"Good luck," I said, as the wheel began to spin. I crossed my fingers.

Suddenly as I watched the spin of the wheel and the blur of the little white ball, I heard a distinct inner voice say, "Quatre!" But I couldn't reach around the man in front of me to place another chip on the board. I quickly turned to Mario. "Bet four," I told him, though usually I didn't speak to him when he gambled. He was superstitious about that. He looked at me questioningly. "I hear a voice in my head that's saying 'quatre,'" I told him.

"Sometimes I think you're really crazy," he said smiling. We both looked up just in time to see the little white ball fall.

"Quatre!!" the croupier called out.

I covered my eyes.

Mario looked at me and frowned.

"It's not me," I defended. "I didn't do anything and I can't control it. Sometimes I just hear the numbers."

"One day somebody's going to kill you," he said.

Frany looked stricken when she didn't win.

Bets were being placed again. I reached across and played my numbers. Mario played his. Frany, with great bravado, put down a bunch more of her chips. This time on different numbers. The ball spun again as we all held our breath.

Mario won a few games, I won a few and Frany just didn't seem to be able to hit a number. Finally, with only a couple of chips left, she placed all she had on the number thirteen, crossed her fingers and closed her eyes. Then she said, "Okay. This time I'm serious. This time I'm going to win."

When the ball fell, it seemed to fall in slot twenty-seven, but then something funny happened. As we watched it was as though some invisible fingers picked it up, carried through the air.... and dropped it in slot thirteen. There was silence for a minute while we all tried to digest what had happened. The croupier bent over the wheel to check and finally shouted, "Trieze."

"Thirteen," I said, excitedly to Frany. "Thirteen!"

She covered her mouth and screamed. The people at the table looked at us. Frany won six hundred dollars that day but she couldn't have been happier if it had been six million.

Chapter 27

The ride to Florence was hair raising for me. We took the auto-strada this time because it was faster than the scenic route and the driver drove as though it was the Grand Prix. I spent the hours scrunched down in the back seat, most of the time with my hands over my eyes. I was too scared to even get carsick. It was on that drive that I made one of my most fervent promises. I swore to the Patriarchal God of old—the white bearded one—that if we got to Florence intact, I would be perfect for the rest of my life.

In the early evening, when we finally arrived at the Excelsior Hotel intact, I knew in my heart it was my Guardian Angel not the driver who got us there.

This hotel was truly elegant. The two-bedroom suite was decorated in light blue velvet and silk, much more down stated and to my taste than the Negresco. All the furniture was white French provincial.

The living room with its white marble fireplace, ornamented with blue scrolling, made the room look like a scene on a Wedgewood china plate. It was bright, airy and soothing.

The concierge was charming and pleasant and offered to make arrangements for the theater, restaurants or sightseeing. When he left the room, all three of us practically collapsed with relief and exhaustion.

"I know there are a zillion wonderful restaurants in Florence," I told Mario. "But just for tonight, can we eat in the room?" Then I turned to Frany. "Would you mind?"

Both of them reluctantly agreed and so we ordered room service.

The dinner was as elegant as the rest of the service at the hotel, and by the time we had finished eating we were refreshed and ready to go out to sightsee.

Mario, Frany and I took a taxi to the Piazzale Michelangelo, where from the square above the muddy Arno river we could overlook the entire city of Florence. In the pink dusk with the falling golden sun glistening on the hundreds of orange terra cotta tile rooftops of the city beneath us, I was breathless. "Wow," was all I could say.

"Quite eloquent, my dear," Mario said, as he put his arm around me.

Frany did better. She was standing on one side of me and Mario was standing on the other.

"Just think, Carol," she said, with reverence in her voice, "of all the artists who stood where we now stand?"

Mario explained, "Artists like Giotto, Fra Angelico, Leonardo Da Vinci, Michelangelo, Raphael, Botticelli." He stopped for a moment and then added, "Sculptors like Donatello and Cellini."

I didn't really get it yet. I just felt sort of dopey that I didn't know.

"Great writers too," he added. "Dante and Boccacio."

In the moment I just wanted to breathe the same air that those great artists and thinkers had. I figured that maybe through osmosis, I could catch some lazy creative thought that had somehow managed to hang around in the atmosphere for the past couple of hundred years and do something with it.

Mario and I were leaning against the cement railing, looking down at the city as darkness fell, and the last of the fading orange light turned everything sort of gold when he explained, "The Medici Dukes and Popes were pretty impressive. Not to speak of those two characters, Savonarola and Machiavelli."

"Machiavelli, I know," I said, relieved, "He's the one who wasn't exactly on the up and up when he wanted something. But Savonarola? I've never heard of him."

Frany laughed. "He was another crazy religious fanatic."

Mario added, "A very colorful religious fanatic, at that. He was a Dominican monk from the monastery of San Marco. A reformer. He was the scourge of luxury. But the poor people loved him."

"Why?" I asked.

"He was a mastermind," Mario said in his mysterious story telling voice. "He was responsible for the great burning of the vanities; wigs, paintings, books, clothes, mirrors, everything that fit his idea of luxury. It was a bonfire held in the Piazza della Signoria."

History was coming to life for me. "Oh, that's what they refer to when they say, "The Bonfire of the Vanities? What ever happened to him?" I asked.

"Justice," Mario said. "They hanged him and burned his body in the same Piazza."

That night, in bed, my mind was spinning. It was so full of thoughts and beauty that it was difficult for me to fall asleep. Mario read for a while, but I laid on my back and just stared at the paintings on the plaster ceiling.

The next morning, Frany, Mario and I left the hotel and walked along the Via della Vigna Nuova, one of the leading shopping streets in Florence. Several small boutiques, windows filled with mannequins dressed in the chicest clothes, lined the narrow street on both sides. I was surprised that everything was so elegant and fashionable. It looked like a magazine spread.

"I like the Naf-Naf's I got in Nice," I said to Mario, reaching for his hand. "Aren't you glad? This stuff is really expensive."

"I'd like to see you in a hat," he said, seriously.

"Mario," I told him, "I'm too short. If I wear a hat, I have to wear heels, I can't run in heels, I can barely walk in heels. Besides, Naf Naf's look like medical scrubs and I love them. Can you imagine that combo?"

He turned to Frany. "She's hopeless," he said.

"But often quite delightful," she said, smiling.

"I'd still like to see her in a hat," Mario repeated.

"Oh God," I said. "I should have played with dolls as a kid instead of hunting and fishing with my father."

Mario looked at me. "Didn't your father wear a hat?"

I smacked him. "Okay," I said, "Let's find a hat. You should have played with dolls."

Between the clothing stores were shops filled with handbags and shoe racks displaying the finest of soft Italian leather.

Shoes and leather are two of my weaknesses. I love the feel of leather and I love shoes that I can run in.

"Let's go in here," I said to Frany, "and see if they have any shoes in my size. I looked at Mario to see what he wanted to do.

"Fine," they both said good-naturedly as they followed me inside.

"Can I help you?" asked the well-dressed saleswoman with a smile. She had a charming accent.

"Can I see all the shoes you have in a size four and a half?" I asked, half expecting her to tell me she had none.

She nodded and asked, "All?"

I thought she hadn't understood me so I just shrugged.

Minutes later, she and two salesmen with shoe boxes stacked too high for them to see over, walked toward me and placed the largest selection of boots, shoes and sandals that I had ever seen on the floor in front of me. I tried on one pair after another, and each fit like Cinderella's glass slipper. For the first time in my life there were enough shoes that fit me to have to make a choice.

Now, I laughed happily as I chose one pair of tan leather and colored tapestry boots and three pairs of sandals: One pair in red, one in white and one in black. The way I figured it I was now set for life as far as shoes went.

Outside again, walking along the street and holding my new treasures, I teased Mario, "Well now at least I know where to go to get shoes to fit me. Florence."

"I guess I'd have to shop in Sweden or Germany," Frany said wryly. "That same store had no shoes in an 11."

Mario stopped at a tobacconist and bought several large Havana cigars. Outside, on the street again, he asked, "What would you like to buy, Frany?"

"When I see it, I'll know," she said.

Just then alongside us a small elegant stationery store seemed to appear. Its window was filled with colorful red papier Mache bulls, teal blue elephants, bright yellow donkeys and other animals. There were marbled papier Mache masks: white comedy masks, and black tragedy masks. Florentine boxes in all shapes and sizes. There were journals and diaries small enough to fit in a pocket and large enough to cover a desk. All of them in lovely pastel watercolors marbleized and melted together to create original designs. No two were the same.

"Oh," Frany said, with her nose pressed to the window, transfixed, "How beautiful. I can get a book to write my poems in, and another to do my sketches."

"Thank God you found something," I said, but Frany was already inside, choosing the gifts to bring to her friends that would help them share the beauty and joy of her trip to Florence.

During lunch at an outdoor cafe in the center of Florence, I asked Mario, "Couldn't we do a little bit of sightseeing together?"

"Certainly," he said pleasantly.

"Really?" I asked, "Or are you teasing?"

I had ordered a fried fish platter and Frany and Mario had ordered pasta. When the fish came, some had been cooked with their heads on. So, I had this huge plate of whole fish and French fries. Mario almost croaked.

"How can you eat anything that stares back at you?" he asked, moving his chair around and turning his back to me.

"Don't be such a sissy," I said.

"I'd hate to be caught out in the open seas on a life raft with her," Frany said to Mario. "She's the closest thing to a cannibal I've ever encountered."

"Guys," I reminded, "Are we going to see some of the art here or not?"

"What do you want to see?" Mario asked.

"The Cathedral, the Bell Tower, and the church where that Saint carried his head to be buried after it had been chopped off" I said.

"Charming," Mario remarked. "And she asks why I'm afraid to close my eyes at night."

"I think she's talking about the church of San Miniato," Frany explained. "It was dedicated to a martyr who was killed under the emperor in the early third century."

"I'll come to the Cathedral and the Bell Tower," Mario volunteered. "But that's where I draw the line."

After lunch, the first thing we saw was the Duomo, otherwise known as the Cathedral of Santa Maria del Fiore. It was right in the center of Florence and so gargantuan it seemed to go on for miles. Outside, the crowds of people looked like a line of ants, so dwarfed were they by comparison.

"Do you believe this?" I said looking up at the huge green and white marble cathedral with its orange dome.

"They started building it in 1296 and it wasn't finished until 1436. It took them one hundred and forty years," Mario said. "That means that the builders who started it never saw it finished. To be a master craftsman is to have patience and endurance" he said. "For true artisans, it's enough to create."

As we walked through the Bronze Doors into the vast Gothic cathedral, I was surprised by how deeply it touched me. Surrounded by statues of familiar saints and angels, I was taken back in time to when I was a child filled with story, innocence and trust; to a time before I needed to think rather than to just believe.

That small and fervent Catholic child I had been was completely awed by the amazing fresco of the Last Judgment. I had always imagined myself to be the one in the painting who reached for God's outstretched hand. He was my God. The God I always trusted to make miracles. This old man with the flowing white beard who I now stood beneath was as immense and as beautiful as I had pictured Him to be. Before feminism. Before I understood that if God was anything at all, he was all aspects of humankind— the feminine as well as the masculine—as well as whatever else.

Still even my childhood mythology wasn't enough to explain my visceral response. Some truth seemed to radiate from the art and the sculpture that penetrated the wall of my mind and touched my soul on a purely aesthetic level.

Suddenly, I felt a part of it. For the first time in my life I had a sense of where I'd come from as a human being. Surrounded by all the religious and mythological figures that were painted and sculpted, I finally had a sense of my own history. Time stopped and I understood the belief systems of those human beings who had come before me.

Angels and saints and the Creator God reached out into their streets to become part of everyday life.

My mind was full, my heart was full and I was truly awestruck. I wanted so much for Mario to share that one enchanted moment. I was feeling terribly sentimental about all of it.

"Why would we believe that as a species we've evolved, that we've made progress?" I asked completely impassioned.

"They had to be a happier people then," Frany added, "with all this beauty around. A soul feels a need for beauty. It's harder to find that in our world today."

Mario was looking around silently. The stained glass of the windows gave the inside of the cathedral an ethereal quality. Rainbow colored shafts of light bounced off our heads like halos.

"How can we think we've evolved?" I repeated with even more passion. "How can we believe that science is more important than art?"

Mario didn't say a word, he seemed to be thinking.

I moved closer to him and reached for his hand. "What do you think is more important, art or science?" I asked looking up at him dreamily.

He looked at me and frowned. "That's a false question," he said, looking straight into my eyes.

"A false question?" I repeated. I didn't even know there was such a thing as a false question.

Mario shook his head. "The real question is, would you give up your central heating and your air conditioning for a poem?"

Chapter 28

The only way to get to the Gritti Palace in Venice from the mainland of Italy was by boat or water taxi. "Are you sure?" I asked the limo driver when we arrived at the dock.

"It's in the center of the sea, Signora," he said shrugging.

"How long a ride is it?" Mario asked. He couldn't swim and neither could I.

"Twenty, thirty minutes..." the driver said casually.

"I'll die," I said. "I can't hold my breath that long."

Frany laughed. "You're such a funny little thing," she said, "You've spent years taking care of patients with meningitis, hepatitis and other terrible communicable diseases which could have been fatal. Yet, now, here, on the way to Venice you get scared. I don't understand you."

"Then, I was working, loving, helping," I explained. "Fate doesn't cut you down in the middle of good deeds. There's not the same protection when you're just out to have fun."

We took a water taxi, a small private motor boat. As it sped through the deep blue sea, tall sheets of water sprayed in foamy white curtains covering the cabin windows. From inside we couldn't see a thing. Mario was sitting across from me on a narrow yellow vinyl bench. Frany sat next to me.

"I must see where we're going," Frany said. She tried to stand but couldn't, because the ceiling was too low. Finally, she made her way up the steps to the deck above.

"I'd rather not know if we're going to go down," I told Mario, as I moved over to sit next to him now.

"You're a girl after my own heart," was all he said.

Suddenly, Frany stuck her head into the cabin. "You must come out and see this," she said. "It's the most magnificent sight you've ever seen."

I held my head and moaned, "Don't force me to do this."

When Frany looked crushed, I thought about how dumb I was acting. After all, I reasoned, the tourist trade in Venice would have dropped significantly if people kept drowning on their way over.

So, I gathered my courage, and stood up.

Mario asked, "Where are you going?"

"To face life head on," I said, and held my nose.

But once on the deck, all I could see for miles around was water. Not even one piece of land. The sheer vastness of it overwhelmed me. I wanted to throw myself overboard just to end the tension.

Mario followed me up onto the deck. I stood hanging onto the rail with Frany on one side and Mario on the other. For what seemed like a very long time, we just stared straight ahead. I listened to the engine and watched the foaming waves as the tiny motor boat cut through the seemingly endless sea.

Suddenly, I saw this incredible vision of a magnificent glimmering city begin to rise up before us. Like some magical sequined dragon, it glistened in the afternoon sun, still wet from the sea as though from its own birthing. Pastel castles with luminous gold and silver rooftops appeared as we got closer. It was so magnificent, it took my breath away. Within me, at that moment, something new had been born.

It was like a too beautiful sunset and it touched my soul like no place else I had ever been. I covered my face and started to cry.

It was then I felt Mario behind me, his hand on my shoulder. He leaned forward and whispered, "You can tell me the truth. Don't you wish you were coming here with someone you were madly in love with? Someone who was the great love of your life?"

I turned and looked at him but nothing in his expression gave him away. He looked so sincere I couldn't help myself.

"No," I said, still sniffling "He wouldn't need the props."

Mario burst out laughing, and swatted me affectionately. "You're funny," he said.

"So are you," I told him.

Within minutes the water taxi was speeding down the Grand Canal, the main highway of Venice, an S shaped waterway lined with palaces. In front of each large stone palace stood a landing stage with green, red or blue striped mooring poles. On top of each pole hung a brightly colored lantern.

Centuries before, men had built this city of 120 small islands on wooden pilings sunk deep in the sea. Gothic palaces, Renaissance public buildings, art galleries, shops, homes and cathedrals all seemed to float.

Mario explained, "Venice was built in the fifth century by Italians who were fleeing the barbarians, specifically, Pepin, the son of Charlemagne. The story goes that twenty years later when the body of St. Mark the Apostle arrived from Alexandria, the city found itself under Divine protection. Venetians believe that protection has helped their city endure all through the years."

Now, the timeless quality of the Byzantine architecture, the rich colors of the Renaissance palaces, and the magnificence of the Gothic Cathedrals, reassured me. That it had survived helped me remember that I was part of, and would always be part of, the most special miracle of God.

Within a few minutes, the launch pulled up to the dock of the Gritti Palace Hotel. The doorman, a handsome young Venetian dressed in a green and gold uniform helped us step out of the boat.

Inside, the concierge, stylishly dressed in a formal black suit with a black and gray stripped tie, was more than courteous. He was thrilled to meet Mario. "Signor Puzo," he exclaimed, with a small bow, "It is a pleasure to have you." Then he told us, "We have reserved for you Signor Hemingway's suite."

Frany whispered, "Oh, isn't this marvelous? Can you believe this?"

I just smiled at her as I took Mario's arm. He's shy and humble and any special recognition seemed to embarrass him. "Are you thrilled?" I whispered to him.

"I'm pleased," he said, smiling. "Maybe I can get some pages done."

This suite was even more luxurious than the others.

White silk and velvet covered all the Queen Ann chairs, the sofa and the king-sized beds in both the bedrooms. Perfect yellow roses stood in tall white china vases on dressers and desks throughout all three rooms. Even the bathrooms—there were three of them—were spectacular. Colored hand-blown Venetian glass was everywhere.

Mario, Frany and I went outside and stood on the terrace. Directly across the canal, we could see the beautiful church of Santa Maria Della Salute. The church that had been built by the survivors of the great plague of the 1600's. The architect had built a wooden dome instead of a stone one to keep the church from sinking even though over a million oak pilings supported it. It was a breathtaking sight.

I turned to Mario, "Thank you," I said, "Thank you for making me come."

"My pleasure," he said.

The following morning, in the lobby, we were introduced to our guide, Carlo. The night before the concierge had insisted, "To see Venice you must have a guide. Carlo is the finest."

Carlo was a distinguished gray-haired gentleman whose whole body was taut with vitality. Venice is hot in July, and muggy. But Carlo looked as though he was climate controlled. He was dressed in a business suit and was carrying an attaché case, as though he was on his way to Wall Street. Now, he smiled in greeting.

As he was introduced to me, he reached to kiss my hand. God, I thought, this is embarrassing, but I stood fast. He did the same to Frany, who looked like she was used to it, and by the time he got around to Mario, Mario was on his way out the door of the hotel.

We followed Carlo for miles along the cobblestone walkways like ducklings after their mother. Carlo turned and watched us with the same concern. Amazingly, there were no cars on the whole island, not one, which changed the landscape completely. The sleek black gondolas, with the singing gondoliers in their straw hats, standing and rowing through the small canals made me feel as though I was in a completely different era. Except for the clothing on the crowds walking through the streets, it could have been the eighteenth century.

There were small boutiques and food stores lining each walkway and stone arch covered alley.

Carlo had us weaving between houses, over bridges, and through palaces as he took us to one magnificent cathedral or church after another. Inside each, he explained in great detail, the beautiful sculptures, extraordinary oil paintings and architecture. He pointed out the burial places of the artists and saints. He recounted the history of Venice including an explanation of the political climate during each period. We marveled at original masterpieces by Tintoretto, Titian, Vivarini, Bellini, Van Dyck and too many others to remember. Carlo, with his bright eyes, expressive features and grand gestures gave us a little biography of each of the great artists. That day he made all of Venice come alive for us.

By lunchtime, Mario, Frany and I were exhausted.

"I will take you to a special place," Carlo told us. "A private trattoria owned by three sisters. They will cook whatever you wish."

That was even more exciting for Mario and Frany than all the other offerings of Venice. Carlo took us to a small restaurant hidden in the midst of Venice. This part of Venice looked completely different from the "tourist" Venice. No crowds at all. As we walked along people greeted Carlo as neighbors would.

At the trattoria one of the sisters greeted Carlo with a big hug and kiss and was so enthusiastic about meeting us that I suddenly felt as though I was in the home of one of my long-lost Italian relatives.

The sister led us to a square table outside under a green umbrella of leaves that had been woven into a trellis. We didn't order, the other sisters just served several dishes family style. Big noodle pasta and small swirls, risotto with peas, spaghetti with red clam sauce, and a large tossed salad made the table look like my mother's on Sunday afternoons. The service was also familiar.

"Eat, eat," one of the sisters who had been circling the table encouraged. Just as I did at home, I ate. It was delicious. The spaghetti was al dente, cooked just perfectly, and the sauce was thick and sweet. As good as my mother's—and that was no small compliment.

Afterwards, we all sat rubbing our stomachs and shaking our heads. Sleepy now, we decided to return to the hotel and take a nap. That afternoon, we made arrangements with Carlo to meet the following morning. We still had to tour the canals and visit the hand-blown glass factory on the island of Murano.

Chapter 29

That evening, after we had supper at Harry's Bar, we walked to Saint Mark's Plaza. It was an immense and regal square bordered on three sides by palatial arcades and on the fourth by the Basilica of St. Mark. That cathedral was the most magnificent I had ever seen. St. Mark the Evangelist's remains were buried here.

As darkness fell, shadows of people sipping coffee and drinks sat like stone statues at the hundreds of small white tables along the border of the square. Under an awning, one on each side, two small orchestras played. The musicians were dressed in white tuxedos with stiff black bow ties. The soft pink spotlights and the mellow strains of the violin music in the background gave the square an aura of fantasy.

"Would you like a drink?" Mario asked us.

"I'd like to sit and listen a while," I told him.

As soon as we sat at one of the small white tables, a waiter seemed to appear. "Beautiful evening," he said smiling.

We all shook our heads in agreement.

Frany took a deep breath and looked around the square. "Isn't it hard to believe we're really here?" she asked.

"Feels like when I was in the army and went into town on a pass with my drinking buddies," Mario remarked.

I looked at him then shrugged my shoulders at Frany. "He's a lovely man, but not really romantic."

Mario looked surprised. "I was talking about the feeling of camaraderie, the feeling of being completely relaxed with buddies. I thought it was a compliment."

"But I thought I was the love of your life," I said. "The girl of your dreams."

"So what?" he said smiling, "Comrades and buddies are special. All that true love stuff is overrated."

Suddenly across the huge square of St. Marks Plaza, the soft poignant strains of the theme from "The Godfather" began to play.

I looked at Frany, she smiled. I looked at Mario, he was subdued.

"Good God, Mario," I said, "Don't you think this is amazing and romantic? We're so far away from home and something you created from a story in your own mind, made it clear across the ocean to Venice."

Mario looked puzzled so I added, "The song, Mario. The theme from the Godfather. Right here, now." It was completely surreal to me.

"Nino Rota composed the score," Mario said. "It's his song, but I must admit, it was perfect for the movie."

My consciousness flipped until my perceptions skipped and I was in a completely different space again. It was as though the art of our time was set against the art of all time, Love and Death the theme.

The following morning, we were awakened by the sound of hammering outside our windows. "What is that?" Mario asked, and I jumped out of bed to open the French doors to the terrace.

"They're building a wooden bridge from this side of the canal over to the church of Santa Maria della Salute," I said to him.

"Must be some kind of celebration," he said.

Frany called in. "Did you see what they've done to the gondolas?"

"I'll be right out," I told her through the door.

Over breakfast in the living room of the suite, Frany told Mario and me, "I shouted down from my terrace to one of the gondoliers to ask what was going on. And he shouted back, 'Big fiesta.'"

"Wonder what that means," I said. It was July 20. Not a Catholic Feast day that I could remember.

Mario offered, "Carlo will know."

I looked at my watch. "He's probably downstairs pacing," I said.

In the lobby, Carlo was waiting. "Good morning, my friends," he greeted us with a wide smile. "Did you sleep well?"

"Like a log," Mario said.

"Until the hammering woke us up," I added.

"Ah," he said, a smile of recognition on his tan face. "The Feast Day of Our Lady of the Plague."

I looked at Frany. Then I looked at Mario. Carlo was already walking quickly out the door to the street.

Once outside he pointed to the wooden bridge. "They are almost half finished," he said. "Throughout Venice on this day bridges will be built across the canals and decorated with laurel and cut flowers. All the gondoliers will dress in costumes and decorate their gondolas. Tonight they will make a procession of boats to the Church of the Redeemer in thanksgiving to Our Lady."

"For what?" I asked as we walked along the flagstone street.

"In 1576 the plague claimed 50,000 lives," he explained. "But it wasn't until the following July that it was decreed to have passed. On the third Sunday, the survivors made a procession to give thanks to the Madonna. It has continued in Venice for these many years."

We took another water taxi and Carlo led us through the vast labyrinth of canals while talking about the history of architecture and the arts. But it was Frany who first saw the bridge.

"Carol, look," she screamed, "The Bridge of Sighs."

I thought she was saying the Bridge of Size. "It doesn't look any bigger than most of the others," I said.

"Sighs," she corrected me, spelling it. The prisoners about to be imprisoned or executed had to cross that bridge." She pointed to the prison. "The ninth and tenth pillars of that building are darker because prisoners were hanged there as a warning."

"Where the hell did you find that out?" I asked her.

She shrugged. "I didn't go to Catholic school. I was educated in England where they teach us history and it has meaning for us," she answered.

Once out of the canals, the boat picked up speed. We were on our way to the island of Murano. "I have a premonition I'm going to drown," I said aloud.

"Not here," Carlo said laughing. "The water is not so deep. Only fifteen feet."

"Well," I said, "That means it's ten feet over my head."

Mario had been sitting quietly the whole time

Standing on the dock we could feel the heat of the blazing fires from the many arched brick ovens and we could see the glass blowers as they turned and clipped and cut the molten glass on their long black iron rods. We watched as they transformed the shapeless masses into beautiful colored vases, fine blue wine glasses and rose-colored lanterns.

I loved the Venetian glass wine sets, especially the deep royal blue with 18 carat gold borders and stems, each one with a painted bouquet on the front. The wine bottle completely gold except for the blue blown glass bowl shaped like a graceful swan.

"Do you like that?" Mario asked me.

"I do," I said.

"Then it's yours," he said and smiled.

"Don't you see anything you like?" I asked him.

"I don't drink wine," he said.

"Neither do I," I said, "but they have to be great for apple juice."

Then Mario saw a large round bowl with yellow and green stripes that seemed to turn to waves as we walked around it. "I love that bowl," Mario said. "I love how the lines seem to come alive."

"That is a collector's original," Carlo explained. "The only one, signed by the creator of this special piece."

I made a face. "What would you do with it?" I asked Mario.

He leaned over and whispered, "Fill it with huge scoops of ice cream." He smiled at Carlo when he said, "I'll take it. A beautiful piece. Thank the artist for me."

Frany was wandering around lifting and touching many of the glass pieces. Finally she picked up a beautiful green glass elephant. "It's got its trunk up for luck," she said showing me.

Carlo talked to the owners while we chose some other glass pieces as gifts for the people at home.

"How can we carry that stuff?" I asked thinking of what would happen to all that beautiful glass in my suitcase.

"We will be happy to ship it," the owner told us. "It will take months but it will get there intact."

We had been around "beautiful" for so long, I had completely forgotten about practical. Even though this was Venice, I had to remind myself, it was still the twentieth century.

For lunch that day, back in Venice, the sisters cooked for us again. Now we all felt like family. Carlo gave us each a gift, and read some letters from other visitors to Venice. He wanted us to remain friends.

When he dropped us off at the hotel, we parted as though he had been our host and he reminded, "Come back again to visit me in Venice. I love to see old friends."

It wasn't until I was lying down for a nap and almost asleep that I remembered. When I did, it was such a shock that I sat straight up. "Mario, it's July 20th," I said. When he didn't answer, I added, "Mario, July 20th is Frany's birthday." I'm terrible about birthdays. I always have been. I try to remember to be nice to people during the year but inevitably I forget birthdays.

"Call room service and order a cake," he said.

Frany was sitting on the couch reading when I got into the living room. She was wearing her white terry bathrobe. "Do you mind if we stay in to eat tonight?" she asked. "I don't feel like dressing for dinner."

"I'd always prefer staying in to going out," I told her, "and from the terrace we should be able to see the boats as they come down the canal."

When Mario came out of the bedroom, he agreed and so we all sat down and tried to figure out what we wanted from room service. Then, through the French doors of the terrace we could hear a chorus of voices raised in song.

"Let's open doors onto the terrace," Frany said getting up. And as she did, I heard her draw in her breath. "Look Carol," she said, then "Mario. Look!"

From the terrace, we could see the terrace of the Gritti Palace dining room below. Delicate metal arches were festooned with laurel leaves and small bright multicolored lights. Each of the old fashioned wrought iron lanterns on the dock were wrapped with colored paper and surrounded by more lights. Candles from the tables flickered in the warm breeze while men in tuxedos and women in beautiful gowns moved to the music on the dance floor like porcelain statues on a music box.

Across the canal, the church of Santa Maria della Salute was completely encircled in white lights, a pink spotlight focusing on the front door and stone carvings of the saints under the huge dome. Down the canal as far as we could see gondolas decorated with pink, blue and yellow paper lanterns and fresh live flowers were gliding in procession, the gondoliers, straw hats bedecked with colored ribbons, rowing slowly and smoothly. Musicians played their mandolins while everyone sang, their heads crowned with laurel leaves, their voices raised in praise. Directly below, a crowd of people, singing hymns and holding candles, walked across the bridge that had been built that day toward the church on the other side.

"What a beautiful sight," Frany said, as she leaned on the stone railing of the terrace. "What beautiful sounds."

Above us just then blue, red, green and yellow fireworks, huge exploding stars in the black night sky, caught our attention. Sparks flew in all directions like giant fireflies, lighting the faces of the singers below and accenting the awe and reverence on their up-turned faces.

"So, you see there have always been plagues," Frany said softly, smiling.

"And there have always been survivors to build monuments and give thanks," I reminded.

"This night could almost make me a believer," Mario remarked.

By the time the doorbell rang, none of us wanted to leave the terrace to eat. Mario walked inside to open the door as Frany and I stayed marveling at the dazzling display of fireworks.

Mario was holding the birthday cake when he called us in to eat. "Happy birthday, Frany," we both said. And then I handed her the Cameo I had bought for her in Florence.

"My birthday," she said, "and The Feast of Our Lady of the Plague in Venice."

"Seems like a great time to ask for a miracle." I said.

Frany looked at me and said, "This is the miracle, Carol. Truly, this is the miracle."

Whenever I remember Frany now, I remember her just as she was on that trip. The picture of her standing on the deck of that watercraft or looking out from the balcony. I can still hear her saying, "Truly, this is the miracle, Carol."

Chapter 30

After that trip, we were both so grateful to get home, to get back to our families and into the routine that made up our real lives.

Mario had finished "The Sicilian" for the hard cover release, and because he was so grateful for my help, he had even dedicated it to me. *For Carol.* I was so embarrassed, that I just mumbled a thank you. It was many years later that I appreciated it enough.

I had finished "Rusty's Story." But not without a lot of grief. The problem was that my publishers wanted me to say that Rusty's epilepsy had been cured, and I wasn't willing to do that.

"I can't," I told Joni.

"It's too frightening the way it is now," she told me. "You'll frighten too many people."

Joni and I were both intractable. "What are we going to do about this...?" I asked her. "We called it non-fiction. There is no cure for epilepsy. So many people have it, I can't lie. I can't pretty it up!"

Joni was tough, but fair. "Let's not kill each other," she said. "I'll let you out of the contract. You can take it straight to Linda Grey at Bantam."

So that's what I did. Linda was happy to publish it, and without any changes that I felt compromised me too much.

I loved that book, and when it was finally released, I got to tour again.

In each of the states that I visited, I met with the people in charge of the Epilepsy Foundation's local chapter.

In every meeting, we talked about the prejudice and the myths that surrounded epilepsy, and the people who still suffered from seizures that could not be controlled by any of the current medications or treatments.

I promised each of them that I would use the media platform I had now in order to educate the public so that if we couldn't stop the seizures, we could at least break down the prejudice that surrounded epilepsy. For three weeks I was everywhere. On TV, on radio, and in print.

But there was one afternoon that really made all the years of struggle and the whole tour worth it. I was in Tampa Florida, meeting with their local chapter. They had invited the patients and patient's families to come to a special hall to meet me. So many had come that I was surprised.

There, after I spoke to them, one little boy about seven years old came over to me. I was speaking to the director, and I felt a little hand tug at mine. I looked down and there he was. Red hair, crazy amount of freckles and tiny pug nose.

"Thank you," he said, with the biggest smile I'd ever see. "You see, I have epilepsy. I always wanted to be a hero. Now, cause of Rusty, I know I can."

He looked so sincere, I asked. "What kind of hero do you want to be?"

"I want to be a real life hero," he said. "Now, I can have a real life!"

That little boy didn't know it, but he carried me throughout the rest of that tour. I may have helped him believe in himself, but he helped me believe in me.

Later that year, Rusty's Story received the National Book Award from the Epilepsy Foundation of America and I was invited to be the keynote speaker at their annual fund raiser. I spoke to an audience of over 400 of the finest neurologists, psychiatrists and clinicians from all over the world.

After my speech was over, many of them came over to thank me for "putting a face" on their diagnosis and each promised they would be far more careful and far more compassionate in treating their patients from that day forward.

But there was even more....

It was cold outside the night Mario came over with a copy of the bestseller list, and he was so excited, he didn't even take his coat off before he said, "Well, we've both made it."

He handed me a framed copy of the latest New York Times Bestseller list. On it, "The Sicilian" was number 9 and "Rusty's Story" was number 7.

Mario had circled both. And, in red felt magic marker on the upper right hand corner he had written, "Anything I can do, you can do better."

That night my heart was full. It had been such a tough battle. I'd had to fight so hard for Rusty and her story and all those others who suffered. It had been such a lot of work. But even though it had been hard, it had been so good for me.

This time I could celebrate. I wasn't alone. I was happy. All I had to do was think about Rusty and that little boy with red hair, and I understood. A book is never only a book, sometimes when you put your own heart and soul into it, you get even more back. Sometimes the heart of God really does reach down to touch the human soul.

Mario and I had to get back to work. Both of us had to concentrate on other books. He had been working on a big canvas book called "The Fourth K" which was not a Mafia book but rather a book about the real possibility he saw of America falling prey to a dictatorship or fascist president.

Two years earlier my grandson Gregory had died of Sudden Infant Death Syndrome and so my daughter, Teri, and I wanted very much to write a book talking about how the tapestry of our family had been changed and offer ways in which we could all heal from devastating loss. We wanted to call that book "Then An Angel Came."

Within a few months, England had bought Rusty's Story, and they were also releasing Mario's The Sicilian.

"Time to go back to London," Mario announced. "Need a few Cuban cigars."

"I could use some English tea.." I said, laughing. "So when do we go?"

"Any day now," Mario said.

Chapter 31

The Ritz Hotel in London is truly snazzy and over the top elegant. Too elegant for me to feel really comfortable in.

Years before Mario and I stayed at another really classy hotel in Paris. We had stayed out late one night for a meeting with Mario's French publisher. In the morning, we had to get up early for another meeting and as we left the room there were two maids in starched brown uniforms walking down the hall in front of us.

As we got closer I heard one of them say to the other in a thick cockney accent, "It's a monkey's cage in there."

We were halfway down the hall before we realized she was talking about our room.

"I told you not to throw your towels on the floor in the bathroom," I said.

Mario shrugged and said, "Remind me never to stay at a four star hotel again. It's uncomfortable when the maids have more class than we do."

Now, years later, Mario and I forgot our rule about 4 or 5 star star hotels. Again, here, everyone walking around the hotel looked as though they were dressed for a formal evening ball. An important one at that. I hated to dress up and so did Mario. Both of us were pretty introverted so neither of us thought of ourselves as one of the "beautiful people."

Mario wore only sweat suits, though they were good sweats like Gucci or Fila, and even when he was motivated to dress up, he'd only concede enough to wear a sports jacket. Of course, no socks—

under any circumstances. He swore they cut off his circulation and made his feet cold.

No matter where we went, his dress code was the same except for the nights he was going gambling. The casinos in Europe are much more formal than the ones in Vegas. Rather than forego the pleasure of gambling, Mario conceded and was willing to wear a tie with his sports jacket.

That night I got him to wear a dark suit. The female croupiers wore long, satin gowns. The chips were more elegant looking too. Whether in London or Cannes the chips were gold embossed. When a player won, there was quiet satisfaction, a nod and a smile, rather than screaming happiness. There's not the same excitement. It's a classy win. A quiet win. An upper class win. That kind of a win is much too civilized to be contagious. It's more fun for me watching people win when they really seem to need the money. Then they jump up and down and scream and pound each other on the back and look really happy.

Anyway, Mario won so we had a happy night. We even left the Ritz, took a taxi over to the Hilton Hotel and Casino and gambled there for another couple of hours. It was less snazzy, brightly lit, and more business-like than mysterious. I was surprised to find that the Ritz held more charm for me. Still, I won more money at the Hilton and it was less intimidating.

After about an hour, we were ready to go back to the Ritz. I had a stack of 100 pound black chips in my jacket pocket.

Good God, I thought, with this amount of money I could buy everyone at home really great presents. But first I had to be sure I could hang on to it. With a bit of restraint I could stay away from the roulette table! I kept repeating over and over, "Not even one last bet."

It took some effort but before I knew it, I was standing at the cashier's cage turning my brightly colored chips into cold hard cash. Great!

Mario cashed in behind me, he had won too.

"How much did you win?" I asked him.

"I'm taking the fifth," he told me.

"You can't do that," I said. "Remember, I get 20% of whatever you win. That was the deal."

"What about all I lost last night?" he asked.

"Hey, don't try to be tricky," I told him. "You made this deal. You know I get a percentage of all you win, and take no responsibility for anything you lose. It's the price of doing business, that's what you said." This time I laughed and Mario just shook his head.

"You're a great closer," he said, and he tousled my hair affectionately.

We were both laughing when we left the casino that night.

On our way back to the hotel, I was chattering, and Mario was happily chewing on his cigar when I absently reached into my blazer pocket and found a lost gaming chip in the seam of my jacket pocket. I pulled it out and looked at it. It was a one hundred pound chip. I held it up and showed it to Mario. I turned around and pointed back at the Hilton. "Do we dare?" I asked, showing him my chip. "Should we try one more time—just to see if we're still lucky?"

"Don't even think about it," he said. "It's a death trap in there. Keep what you've got and let's escape with our lives."

"But we're leaving London tomorrow," I said. "I won't get a chance to bet it."

"Save it for next time," he said. "Consider it a lucky chip."

"Okay," I said. "Done." I dropped it back into my pocket.

It was a beautiful clear balmy night as we walked back to our hotel, and even Mario was chatty. At 2 in the morning, the immaculate London streets were peaceful and empty.

"Wonder why I feel so safe here. Could it be just because the streets are so much cleaner than at home?" I asked him.

"There are Bobbies hiding around every corner," he said. "That's why you feel safe."

"I don't think so," I told him. "I've never even seen one cruising around at night."

As we passed the small closed boutiques, and jewelry shops, I noticed several homeless people huddled in the doorways sleeping. Their clothes and other belongings were heaped in mounds around them far enough off the sidewalk not to cause a problem.

One woman hidden in the shadows of the shop doorway caught my eye. It looked as though she'd stepped straight out of a Dickens' novel. I felt moved by her and drawn to her. As though hypnotized, I stopped walking and moved closer, because something about her fascinated me. Thin and very old, with a clean blue bandana wrapped around her head, her face was a painted canvas lined with life. She was sitting upright against a bundle of clothes propped against a wall. As I watched, her head dropped forward and she fell asleep.

Without thinking, I walked over to her and patted her gently so as not to frighten her. "Hi," I said, to her smiling. "I want to give you something." I took the chip out of my pocket and pressed it into her palm, noticing as I did it, how bony her hand was, how thin and cold her skin.

She looked up at me, questioning. "Have a good day tomorrow," I said. "I won it at the Hilton so they'll cash it for you."

It was then she looked down at the chip in her hand. "Wait," she called after me, because I was already running trying to catch up with Mario. "Girly, wait," I heard her call again.

I stopped. "What is it?" I asked, turning and walking back toward her.

"There's something wrong here, girly," she said. "This is a hundred..."

"I know," I told her. "I want you to have it."

"Why Girly?" she asked. "Why me?"

"Because you're living your life, and I'm living mine," I said. "I'm grateful to you."

She laughed then, and it was a beautiful, full-hearted laugh. "I thank you Girly. I do. May God keep blessing you then."

"And you," I said, smiling back.

When I finally caught up with Mario, he was frowning. "You're going to get into trouble one of these days, talking to everyone."

"She was great," I told him. "I gave her my lucky chip, and she was thrilled."

"She thought you were crazy," he said simply.

I shrugged. "Don't know, but she did say 'God Bless you.'"

"See," he said. "She felt bad for you because she knows you're crazy."

"I don't care," I told him, reaching for his arm, "I feel more blessed by her prayer than by any I've heard in church."

We walked the few blocks left to the hotel in silence. But just as we walked into the enormous front lobby I asked Mario, "Do you really thinks I'm nuts?"

"I don't get altruism," he said. "I don't have any understanding of that virtue."

"How can that be?" I asked him. "You're one of the most generous people I've ever met."

He didn't respond except to say, "That's because I'm rich now. Do you know why governments run welfare programs?"

"To help people who can't help themselves?" I said.

"To keep them from revolution," he said simply.

Chapter 32

The year we rented Burgess Meridith's house, Mario was working hard on finishing his book, "The Fourth K". We had gone to Reno that year so Mario could work with Francis Coppola on Godfather III. But once in Malibu Mario promised himself that he would focus on his book before he lost energy around it.

I was upstairs on my computer typing one of the final drafts of The Fourth K, when the phone rang. Lanetta was at the market getting some fresh vegetables to help make Mario healthy so I answered the phone.

"Hi," I said.

The voice on the other end of the phone was both warm and confident. Funny mix. "This is Frank Mancuso," he said. "Is Mario there?"

"Sure," I said. I walked to the top of the stairs to call for Mario but he was already halfway up the stairs. I covered the phone and whispered. "It's Frank Mancuso."

Mario lay on the bed and I handed him the phone to talk.

Once back at my computer, I could hear Mario talking softly in the background. "Yes, Frank. Certainly I understand. I know what you mean." From across the room I could hear a voice through the phone speaking excitedly. I listened as Mario reassured him. But finally I heard Mario say, "Francis is a fine director. Maybe he has something in mind we can't yet see. Once its on the screen maybe he'll fool all of us."

That always made me shiver. I hated that Mario always backed Francis when I'd heard so much from so many people about how Francis never gave Mario credit for what I believed he deserved. Still, on the other hand, I knew how important marketing was to any project, and Francis did put himself out to market the projects. So half of me understood how infuriating Mario must have been for Francis. Still, I didn't forgive him.

When Mario finally hung up, he was still lying on the bed, but now he was holding his head.

"What's up?" I asked. "Who's Frank Mancuso?"

Mario raised his eyebrows. "He's head of Paramount. Godfather III is his movie now."

"God," I said. "And the problem is?"

"Francis wants Michael to commit suicide and his daughter, Mary, to get shot."

"Why?" I asked. "Sounds existential. It also sounds like 'the sins of the father shall be visited upon the daughter,' etc. But how does he think that will serve this male myth. Retribution?"

Mario got off the bed, and reached for a cigar. Slowly he lit it, thinking. I tried to be patient. Finally, he said, "Francis is going for a literary ending, and it's not dramatically effective."

"Too vague for me to learn anything from," I said, spinning my computer chair around to face him. "How do you feel about it? What do you think?"

Mario sat down on one the chairs opposite me. "I'm completely against it," he said. "I think after three movies, the audience needs catharsis." He leaned back and raised his eyes toward the ceiling deep in thought. "I feel that Michael should have to pay for his sins, that's true. That's storytelling. But I think visually and Francis is way off base on this. I think there should be a big funeral cortege in Sicily after Michael is dead. Black horses pulling an old-fashioned black carriage with a simple coffin covered with flowers. Like the Kennedy thing. A cortege of people crying and mourning one of their favorite sons. That would be more dramatically effective."

I frowned. "Mario, you never even raised your voice. If that's what you believe, why don't you fight for it? Your name is on this screenplay too. I don't get it."

"It's Francis' movie," he said simply. "As a novelist I don't want anyone to tell me how to write my books. As a director, Francis gets final say on the movie."

"But maybe he'll see it your way if you're more impassioned about it. Maybe he'll get it and then you'll both have a better movie."

"I have to work on my book here. I'm almost finished," he said.

"I lost some piece of this conversation," I said. "I'm not following you."

"Frank wants me to go to Rome and try to talk Francis out of killing Mary and suicide, but I can't do it because of the book. 'The Fourth K' still needs some work and I can't lose my focus by going to Rome."

"Mario," I told him, "If it was my movie and I felt as strongly about it as you do, I'd fight so Francis could try to see it. Besides in this case I do believe you're right. I believe a huge funeral cortege in Sicily would give closure that his ending won't. I mean as a storyteller, I think his way is the wrong way to go."

Mario looked up at me steely eyed. "When you make your movie, when you write your book, you can fight for it. I fought for my book. I won't fight for a movie. It's a director's medium."

"Fine," I said, frustrated. "Let him ruin it. But I don't understand your loyalty to him."

Mario smiled. "I still owe him for keeping faithful to my book in Godfather I & II. He did things that only a great director could do and those are movies you can watch. So I forgive him for whatever he does with Godfather 3."

"But both your names are on the credits," I said. "It will make you look bad too."

Mario shrugged. "I can't worry about that. You always have to be more careful when you're innocent than when you're guilty," he said.

"You drive me crazy," I told him.

He frowned. "What's it got to do with you?"

"It offends my sense of justice and fairness," I explained.

"We're talking about two different things," he said. "We're not talking about justice here, we're talking about art. An artist sees things the way he does. That's it."

The phone rang again. This time it was Al Pacino. He talked to Mario. He wanted to know what Mario thought and he wanted Mario to talk to Francis.

The third phone call was from Frank Mancuso again. He really wanted Mario to go to Rome to talk to Francis.

Mario just shook his head. "I'm a writer," he said. "I have a book to finish. I can't be running around Rome trying to change somebody's mind about something that's not my business. If Francis asks, I'll tell him what I think. But no matter how much advice you give them, people always do what they want to do."

With that Mario sat down at his table, straightened his glasses and began to edit the pages of his manuscript.

Chapter 33

We had been going to England and Cannes every spring for so many years now that I was finally getting more comfortable with it. In fact, I even learned to enjoy some of it. Not the celebrity of it, but England and France itself. I loved the difference in the foods, the small outside cafés and everything that was so different from my life at home.

The morning after we arrived in Cannes, the lemon yellow sun forced its way through the shutters waking me up. During the film festival, it was almost impossible to find a place to stay, no matter how far In advance the arrangements are made so this time we tried this new hotel, The Martinez.

I laid on the white and gold chaise and began to read. Mario was still asleep so I called downstairs for Room Service. By the time breakfast arrived, Mario was awake.

Over a breakfast of red orange juice, flakey croissants, sweet butter and tea, Mario asked me, "What do you feel like doing today?"

"I'd like to go to Nice, look around for my NAF NAF's, eat lunch and maybe pick up a few things for the people back home," I suggested, "How does that sound?"

"We have no more room in our suitcases," Mario said from behind his newspaper.

"Well, I thought if we could pick up some special porcelain pieces like Lladro's, Limoges or Waterford, that would be fun for them to keep. Things that they could treasure that they wouldn't go out and buy for themselves. Not so personal that we can't get several different things, like ashtrays, tea pots, statues, you know and decide who to give them to when we get home."

"The suitcases are full," he reminded me.

"That's okay," I said, "If I find some things I really like I can buy another suitcase here with wheels…"

"I won't carry a suitcase through the streets of Nice," he said.

"I don't mind," I said. "I will."

"Well then you can't walk with me," he said. "You'll make me *scumbadi*," A word Mario always used to mean "embarrass me big time or even more concise 'lose face.'"

"I'll pretend I don't know you," I said. "Or I'll pretend I'm a Chinese wife and walk behind you, several steps. I'll practice."

"You've got a deal," he said.

That afternoon we walked down the narrow back streets behind the Promenade de Anglais looking through the small shop windows until I finally found a couple of pairs of NAF-NAF's—funny cotton lounge suits that looked like surgical scrubs. They were the most comfortable clothes I'd ever had.

Afterwards, we stopped at a small sidewalk café. Outside there were stalls of freshly caught fish packed in ice and lots of colorful crisp vegetables and fruit.

"I love the idea of choosing my own fresh caught fish and fresh picked vegetables to eat," I said. "It's seems so healthy, I feel virtuous."

"I don't like fish," Mario said. "I never had it as a kid, and I can't eat it now."

"Order pizza?" I said. "Or some other kind of spaghetti. It's better in France than in Italy, remember?"

We sat through a leisurely lunch, talking, laughing and really enjoying ourselves.

I love French food, especially fish. Rich creamy sauces of which I only take a few bites before I feel totally sated. Mario was so happy with his pizza and calzone, that he tipped the waiter even more than usual.

As we got up to leave, I noticed two young well dressed men sitting in a booth by the front door. I smiled at them but they just lowered their eyes and went back to sipping their wine.

Once outside again, the street was filled with shoppers. I was excited about looking for the Limoges and Waterford crystal. There was a little store, filled to brim with crystal and fine bone china and porcelain. Reasonably priced. A wonderful little French woman, Madame Touret, the shopkeeper, told us she had been there for years, but the most interesting thing about her was the stories she told about her travels as she discovered each piece.

While Mario listened to her, I ran outside without a word, across the street to a luggage store and found the suitcase I would need to take the presents home. A big silver aluminum one, light as a feather and lined with foam. Just what I would need to get everything home safely. Tickled, I said to the shopkeeper, "Too bad it has no wheels.."

"Ah..Madame, but we have another," he said. "Just a wee bit larger."

It truly was not too much bigger but even at that it was half the size of me. Still, it did have wheels. So I took it.

"I'll bet you never even noticed I was gone," I said to Mario as I ran into the store again. I tried to keep the silver suitcase behind me.

"Whose refrigerator are you wheeling?" he asked.

"Good God, I swear you wouldn't believe how light it is," I said, but when I turned to show him, he was already lifting a bunch of faded francs out of his wallet.

"My dear, I wish you well. Enjoy yourself shopping," Mario said, "See you back at the hotel." I dropped the suitcase where it was, and ran after him.

"Wait," I said. "I know what I want, I'll just be a minute."

Mario looked at his watch. "I'll give you five my dear, for I'm a patient man. But then I must be on my way. Alone."

I chose the presents I wanted, filled the suitcase quickly wishing I had some bubble wrap, and ran out the door just as I saw Mario walking down the street.

I was muttering to myself about how much of a pain he was—not wanting to be seen with me because of the damn suitcase, when I noticed the two young men I had seen at the restaurant. They were walking slowly behind Mario. But after a few minutes, one of them crossed the street to the other side and I wondered why, because he seemed to be keeping in step with his friend. As I watched, Mario stopped in the archway of an antique leather goods store to look in the window, and right behind him, really close, came the first young man.

Suddenly there was a big commotion, and as I watched I could see Mario clutching the young man's arm, holding it high in the air. A woman hit the young man with her pocketbook and he began to holler in French.

Mario held tight.

An older man came up behind the younger one and quickly hit him with his cane uttering a loud reprimand. Then he lifted his hand to call "Gendarme. Thief!!!"

Mario let go of the young man's arm, and I could hear him say. "Run, you dope. Haven't you ever heard of white collar crime?" But the crowd was enraged and some of them began to chase the man.

"What happened?" I asked Mario.

"I reached into my pocket to pull out my wallet, and touched what I thought was a mouse," he said. "But when I wrapped my fingers around it, they were fingers. That dumb kid's fingers. He was trying to pick my pocket."

"What was he screaming about?" I asked.

"He kept insisting 'It was not me...It was not me'. But I was holding the hand that was in my pocket." Mario was laughing. "Can you believe that? Even with all the proof, he kept insisting he was innocent." Then he frowned and looked at me. "Where were you?" he asked.

"Behind you, looking as though I didn't know you. Minding my business. Oh, and watching those guys follow you and set you up..."

"Why didn't you warn me?" he asked.

"I don't talk to strangers," I said.

After that we walked back to the hotel together and Mario seemed much less embarrassed than he thought he would be.

Chapter 34

Back home again, on Long Island, we got into our usual routine. It was a Saturday night, so I was sleeping over at Mario's, but he was having a hard time falling asleep. He was in really bad pain. His legs felt so hot they were on fire, he said, and it was keeping him awake. He kept tossing and turning in bed. I gave him a Percodan for pain, and a long backrub. Then we clicked on the TV and watched a double feature. By the time we shut off the lights to try to sleep it was 3 am. But within minutes he was tossing and turning again.

"Any ideas?" I asked.

"Maybe a hot bath," he said.

"Okay." I said as I jumped out of bed and walked toward the bathroom. "I'll draw your water, Mon ami."

"Honey, I don't want to keep you up too," he said. "You can sleep in the study. You know, I sometimes have nights like this."

I was already kneeling on the floor in the bathroom running the water into the sunken tub. "How hot?" I asked.

"Warm," he said. "No too hot tonight."

I walked back into the bedroom and was about to climb back into bed while waiting for the bath to fill when Mario asked, "Hey kid, how about helping me up? I seem to be having some trouble."

"Sure," I said. "No problem." I smiled a reassurance.

"You're a better nurse than a girlfriend," he teased. "Much more cooperative and pleasant."

"And my love, you are a much better patient than a guyfriend," I said. "Much more accommodating and grateful."

I reached down to help Mario lift his legs off the bed. They seemed too heavy for him to move easily. It was automatic for me and I wasn't paying much attention, the nurse in me was always 'at the ready.' When I helped Mario stand, I noticed his legs were weak. And his gait was strange.

"What's with your legs?" I asked him.

"Don't know," he said, "they feel funny. I can't trust them."

"Okay," I said, moving to his side and holding his arm. "I'll hold you up."

He turned and smiled at me. "You really are a terrific nurse," he said again.

"No problem," I said. "It's my nature. Besides, nursing is the one area that has never impaired my power position. I'm happy to be of service. Truly."

"You're a very funny girl," he said, as I helped him step down into the tub. It was difficult to maneuver him because he had to rest most of his weight on me in order to step down and it would have been impossible if his son, Eugene, hadn't had the metal rail put on the wall alongside. With me on one side bracing his leg with my own, he could balance himself. Mario continued, "I take you to the best places in the world, feed you the finest foods, offer you maids, and you're a pain in the ass. But here, you're a nurse, and you never complain."

"That other stuff is hard for me," I told him. "This is easy."

I held onto his arm as he lowered himself into the water, slowly. "Can you grab that book I was reading and bring it to me?" he asked.

"Sure," I said, as I walked back into the bedroom. On his nightstand, there were several stacks of books. "Which one?" I asked.

"The one by Fay Weldon," he said, loud enough for me to hear.

I picked up the book and walked back into the bathroom.

I leaned down to give it to him but he reached up for the book with dripping hands. I automatically grabbed a dry washcloth and handed it to him. "Want to dry your hands first so your pages don't stick?"

"Thanks," he said, and wiped his hands.

Inside that bathroom there was a large shelf stuffed with bath towels and bath blankets. I grabbed a big purple bath blanket and threw it on the tile floor next to the tub. Then I went back into the bedroom and grabbed my pillow and my book.

When I got back, Mario was holding his book above the water, but he wasn't reading. His eyes were closed and his pain was etched in the tight lines around his mouth.

I threw my pillow on the bathsheet and lay down. "Anything I can do for you?" I asked.

He didn't open his eyes, he just shook his head.

I began to read. Suddenly I turned to see Mario looking at me.

"What?" I said. "You don't want me in here?"

He smiled. One of his rare, undefended, authentic smiles. "I want you in here," he said. "But I don't understand why you'd want to be in here lying on a cold tile floor when you could be in a nice soft warm bed."

"I'm keeping you company," I said.

Mario began to read again. After a few pages he turned to me and asked, "Could you let a little more hot water in?"

"Sure," I said getting up and turning on the faucet by his feet. It ran slowly into the tub but I waited, checking the water temperature. If Mario's legs had diminished sensation because of his diabetes, I didn't want the water to burn him.

After a few minutes, I asked. "Warm enough?"

Mario nodded. "Yes," he said. "It's good."

"Want something to drink?" I asked.

"A Pepsi would be nice," he said.

I walked into the study, grabbed a soda from the small refrig that his kids kept filled, and poured it into a glass. Then I walked back into the bathroom and handed it to him. "Just give it back when you're finished," I said.

I laid back on the floor, rearranged my pillow, and began to read.

When Mario handed me back the glass, I just put it on the ledge of the tub between us. He smiled at me.

"What?" I asked.

"Did you do this with other patients, as a nurse?" he asked me.

I started to laugh.

"Really," he asked. "Did you?"

I sat up and folded my legs yoga style. "What kind of a girl do you think I am?" I said, with mock horror. "Do you think I'm the kind of girl who'd lie on a cold tile floor in the middle of the night next to any naked man? I thought you knew me better."

"You can tell me the truth," he said, and he sounded serious.

"I can't," I said. "I really can't. It's much too personal." As I laid back down and picked up my book again all I could do was shake my head and laugh some more.

"You mind reading to me?" Mario asked after a little while.

"No," I said. "Your book or mine?"

"Did you ever read Fay Weldon?" he asked.

"No," I said. "I don't even know who she is."

Mario smiled. "She's a very cheerful feminist who doesn't hate men. And she's got a great sense of humor."

"Okay," I said. "I'll read it to you now if you like. Maybe it will take your mind off the pain in your legs."

For the next two hours I turned the faucet on several times to keep the water warm, brought Mario pills whenever the pain got really bad, and gave him Pepsi to drink. In between, I laid on the floor and read to him.

It was dawn by the time I'd finished the book. I was tired and Mario's legs finally stopped hurting. Just before I got up, he looked over to me and smiled. Then he reached out and affectionately patted my hand.

"This is a love story," he said, "But it hasn't been written yet."

"We're a little old for Romeo and Juliet," I said. "And I never really liked that story. It ends badly."

Mario smiled. "This isn't Romeo and Juliet," he said. "It's a Neil Simon."

"So write it," I said. "If you can see it, you should write it."

Mario shook his head. "It's beyond my powers," he said simply.

"I don't get it," I said. "You're a really good writer."

But Mario said, "Still, love stories don't play to my strength. A crime writer writes mysteries, a romance novelist writes romances, some writers write only non-fiction. I write about the dark side of human nature."

"That's not completely true," I said, "or your bad guys and crooks wouldn't be likable and sympathetic. You just make them mythic."

"That's true," he said. "But I don't really capture women because I don't understand them well enough. So, if I wrote about us, everyone would hate you."

"Not if you really loved me," I said. "It would come through. You said you can't lie on the page. You said you can tell stories and you can weave magic spells to get readers to suspend their disbelief, but you can't really lie."

"That's true," he said. "But I've also said you should only write what you know."

"But Mario," I protested, "even from a story standpoint how would painting me as the bad guy make sense? You would make yourself a hero, and your audience would think you were a dope because you had lousy taste in women? That's not good storytelling."

"See, that's why I can't write it," Mario said. "You write it. It's easier to make me sympathetic."

I frowned. "You've got to be kidding, right? Why would that be?"

He laughed now. "Because I don't talk that much."

I was helping Mario out of the tub when I asked, "Why do you think they'd hate me if you wrote about me?" I grabbed one of the big towels to dry him off.

"Because you say such terrible things," he said. "And nobody can see your angelic smile."

"It's true," I said, "and yet it seems such a shame that one of the great love stories of contemporary times will go unwritten just because you won't do it."

When he got back into bed, and was finally comfortable, he smiled at me. "You write it," he said. "Get out there and stand for us."

"If you can't write it what makes you think I can?" I asked.

"History. Intuition. Tradition," he said. "By definition you write inspirational tragedies about heroes. That's a love story. It's writing to your strength."

Just before I fell asleep, I said aloud. "I'm calling the neurologist tomorrow and making an appointment for you to see him. Gary's a really good doctor and I want to know what's going on."

"I don't want to see a doctor," Mario said.

"I know," I told him. "But I'm not watching you suffer any more. I'd rather kill you than watch you in pain."

"See what I mean about the things you say?" Mario said. "Now I have to sleep with one eye open."

"Or agree to see a doctor," I said. I reached over to kiss him on the forehead, "Night honey," I said.

"Night angel," he said. It was already light out before we finally fell asleep.

Chapter 35

Mario was really excited to get to the tables on on our next trip to Vegas. He had been working really hard on his book, "The Last Don," and was looking forward to having some fun. Gambling eased his anxiety whenever he was writing.

Vegas was also a great escape for me, finally, away from all the duties of my own dynasty, as Mario referred to the family. Besides, the weather was hot, and I loved escaping the cold weather in New York. I had learned to like roulette, it gave me a chance to practice "hearing" the numbers and maybe win a little money which I could share with my family when I got home.

The Sands considered Mario a "high roller" and so they always sent a limo to the airport for him. This time it was a long white one. The driver was pleasant and impeccably dressed. He was making small talk with Mario about the changes in Vegas now that business had taken over. "Not the same as the old days," he said.

Though the Sands had built a huge new tower right off the main casino, we often stayed in the same suite on the main floor of the bungalows in the back. Each suite was named after a famous race-horse, each decorated differently.

Secretariat was the one we liked best.

As Mario signed in at the front desk, the clerk didn't seem to recognize him. Though he was polite, when Mario said, "The Secretariat Suite in the bungalow..." the clerk cut him off with a crisp, "Sorry sir, that suite is taken."

Mario seldom complained about anything but I could see him frown when he told the young man without raising his voice, "I reserved that suite when I called."

The clerk nodded as he searched his computer screen to see what he could find. "We have a lovely suite in the main casino hotel," he said.

Mario said, "We always stay in the bungalows."

The clerk continued to search his screen for vacancies and he offered us several other suites but Mario was more adamant than I had ever seen him.

"Get me the casino boss," he said, quietly to the clerk.

The final disrespect for Mario was when the clerk said, "Could you stand aside sir, to wait so I can check these other folks in?"

Mario walked quickly away from the desk, through the casino and into the pit, where the casino boss was sitting on a high chair overlooking all the tables.

"Hey Mister P," he said, greeting Mario cheerfully. He turned toward me and smiled. "Mrs. P. How have you been?"

"Good," I said. I nodded and smiled.

As Mario walked over to him, the Pit boss beckoned to another man across the room and got down from his chair to shake Mario's hand. "What can I do for you Mr. P? Anything."

Mario looked serious as he took the casino boss aside. I stood back. The only thing I could hear was Mario saying, "What the hell happened to this place? Who the hell is running it?"

"Businessmen," the pit boss said. "It's corporate now."

As they walked across the casino toward the front desk, I walked behind them.

I managed to see the casino boss shrug and say. "It's a new world. They use the bottom line like a gun, none of the old courtesies. It's changing Mr. P."

The casino boss got Mario the suite across from Secretariat, a mirror image, called Seabiscuit, and Mario was grateful to the man, though he was still aggravated by the change.

"You're upset?" I asked, as we walked toward the luggage station.

"They're going to wind up giving me a heart attack," he said.

As the bellman loaded our luggage into the back seat of the white golf cart for our ride to the bungalow, Mario was chewing hard and fast on his large black cigar. Once there, as we walked down the hall toward our suite, I noticed he was breathing hard. Under his breath, Mario was muttering about businessmen being worse than the old mafia with none of the loyalty or charm.

"Want to slow down a little?" I asked.

"No," he answered, "I've got to get my wallet to tip the bellman." Mario always wore sweat suits to travel and gamble so he never kept his wallet in his pocket.

As soon as we were settled in the room, Mario lay on the couch. I brought him a Coke, and asked, "You feeling okay?"

His color was pasty, his lips bluish.

"I'm fine," he said. "I just got to get to the tables and do a little gambling. It's good for my nerves."

I walked over and sat on the couch next to him, and then I reached for his wrist so I could take his pulse. Right now my fingers felt a pounding but irregular heartbeat.

"Maybe we should rest a little while before we go back to the casino," I suggested. I wanted time for his heart to slow down.

He studied me, but didn't say anything.

I leaned down and put my head on his chest.

"What's wrong?" he asked.

"What do you mean?" I asked.

He stroked my hair but he said, "When I first knew you, I used to think your head on my chest was a sign of affection. Now I know you're listening to my heart. So what's the verdict?"

"It sounds like you need to rest a little before you go into battle," I said. "I hear something." What I heard was irregular beats and then a galloping heart. I picked my head up and looked at his face. I didn't love the color of his lips and his skin was getting dusky. "Let's order room service, eat something, take a nap, and then reconsider."

"There's nothing to worry about," he insisted. "I'll be fine."

"Okay," I said. "But then I'd like to rest a little bit so I have enough energy to gamble and win."

He laughed. "It's all in the hands of the gods," he said.

"Maybe so," I said. "But sometimes they can use some help."

We ate, napped for a couple of hours, and then walked up to the main casino to gamble. By then the sun had gone down. It was a beautiful night, warm and breezy, overhead a clear velvet black sky dotted with stars.

Once in the casino, Mario moved toward the tables more slowly than usual. I tried not to worry when he spent most of his time at the Baccarat table, sitting, rather than running from one craps table to another or playing roulette.

Later, on the walk back from the casino to our suite, Mario said, "Let's fly to Laughlin tomorrow to gamble."

"What's Laughlin?" I asked, "You've never mentioned it."

"It's little gambling place right on the border in California," he explained.

"I don't want to fly to Laughlin," I said. "Not until I know you're okay."

"I feel fine," he said.

I laughed at him. "That's because you're not getting enough oxygen to your brain," I told him. "Your color is lousy and I don't like your heart rhythm."

"Gambling cures everything," he said.

"Pitch it to me tomorrow," I said. "Once I can get a handle on this..."

That night we got into bed early but still, I was uncomfortable with the sound of Mario's breathing. It was what in medicine we'd call "wet." Like breathing through water. Also, he was restless, he couldn't lay still, he kept tossing and turning. Finally he jumped up.

I turned on the light. "Mario," I said. "I don't like the way you sound or the way you look. Sit down and let me take your blood pressure."

He sat down obediently and I tried to take his blood pressure and pulse. His blood pressure wasn't really bad but his pulse was so erratic I couldn't even count it. Also, his nostrils were flaring—a dead giveaway to air hunger.

"I want to call a doctor," I told Mario. "Just to have him check you."

"No," he said. "I'm okay."

"You are not okay," I told him. "What about a quick visit to the emergency room?"

He shook his head. Then he started to cough- a wet cough.

"Mario," I said. "All that gurgling sounds like pulmonary edema—heart failure in regular terms, so you really should go..."

He looked at me horrified. "I can't do that," he said. "You know how embarrassing that would be? Think of the Headlines. 'Godfather Dies In Vegas While Gambling.' Can't do it, it's too humiliating."

But later that night, I called the front desk and asked if they had a doctor on staff. They sent two security guards back to the cottages to take Mario to the ER but he refused to go with them. He told them to leave the room, and he would call if he really needed them.

I was frantic. "I'm going to call the kids," I told him.

"If you do that, I won't ever take you with me again," he said.

"Don't threaten me," I said, a little too sharply. "That's no punishment if you wind up dead."

"Honey, don't yell," he said. "You'll give me a heart attack. Don't you have anything I can take?"

I shook my head and tried to think. Then I gave him a Lasix, a diuretic to help lessen the load on his heart. He took a Valium that his doctor had given him, and went back into bed. Finally, he fell asleep. But I stayed awake.

An hour later, I called Lanetta.

"We need a heart specialist," I said and told her the story. "Do you know one?"

"I'll find the best one and get Mario an appointment for tomorrow," she said.

"He wants to go to Laughlin to gamble," I said. "So we'll have to fight first."

"Oh dear," she said, concerned, "I hope you can make him do the right thing." She hesitated before she added, "I'm sure you can convince him."

Mario slept the whole night while I stayed awake watching him breathe. In the morning when he woke up, he said, "Good. I feel better. Let's go get some pancakes.'

Actually, he looked pretty good, which played with my head.

"I'll order room service," I volunteered, trying to save him the walk to the casino. I figured that over breakfast I could tell him about the appointment with the doctor.

But Mario wanted to eat in the coffee shop. He loved the morning light coming in that room at the casino, and wanted another chance to try his luck at the tables.

Eating breakfast went well. The food was delicious, I had steak and eggs and fresh fruit from the buffet. Mario had his usual—pancakes. His appetite was better than the night before and all he was talking about as he ate was going to Laughlin.

"Let's spend a couple of hours at the tables," Mario said, walking into the casino. He played both roulette and baccarat, and lost on both tables. His breathing was labored though I tried not to notice.

"Maybe I'll be luckier in Laughlin," he said. He was walking away from the roulette wheel when he said, "Let's go back to the suite. I'm tired."

He stopped at the front desk to talk to the concierge and while I waited, I put the extra coins I had in my pocket, into one of the big slot machines in the front lobby.

Suddenly there were flashing lights and clanging bells. I'd hit the jackpot. I won 1000 silver dollars. That machine was spitting them out faster than I could grab them so they were spilling onto the floor. I ran over to grab Mario. "We have to get out of here before I lose it again."

Mario smiled. "Maybe you'll be lucky in Laughlin too," he said.

We were walking back to the suite, when I stopped. Mario was breathless again.

I shook my head. "I'm not flying to Laughlin," I said. "I told you that. So if you insist on going, you go alone."

He turned and looked at me. "I know you told me you wouldn't fly to Laughlin," he said. "That's why I asked the front desk to order us a Limo."

At this point I was so worried that my hands were flying all over as I talked. "Mario," I said. "You are not well. I am not taking the responsibility for you when in my very best judgment you should be seen by a cardiologist. It's way too reckless."

"I feel fine," he said. "I'm old that's why I'm huffing and puffing."

I reached over and held his wrist with my fingers, taking his pulse again. "You're only a couple of days older than last week, which is not that old. Your pulse is all over the place," I told him. "Your heart is not pumping effectively and you're not getting enough oxygen." What I really meant was that if those irregular heart beats got any closer together he would be in a fatal arrhythmia and we would no longer have a choice.

Mario gave me a stony look, his horse's head look. "Don't even," I said to him. Then I got a grip on my emotions. I didn't want to aggravate him so much he really would have a heart attack and then through some crazy trick of thinking, I'd believe I caused it. I took a deep breath, and patiently said, "Okay, let's try to compromise."

By now we were back inside the suite. Right inside the entrance, there were two large closets with mirrored sliding doors. I turned the light on, and standing behind Mario I put my hands on his shoulders and turned him around to face the mirror.

Then I put my fingers on his lips. "Okay, help me diagnose. What color are this man's lips?"

Mario tilted his head, staring at himself. "You're right," he said. "They do look a little blue."

His nostrils were flaring, each time he took a breath.

"Do you know why they're blue?" I asked.

"Not enough oxygen?" he said. "Right?"

"Right," I said.

"Okay. Now, if we agree you're not getting enough oxygen, and that you are unwilling to go to a hospital in Vegas because you'd be too embarrassed to die here—rather than declaring you impossible or incompetent—can I ask one more question?"

"Can I stop you?" he asked, coughing.

"Probably not," I admitted. "Here goes. My question: If you fall down on the floor right now, what do you want me to do? Do you want me to just hold your hand and comfort you while you take your final breaths and slip into the next world, or do you want me to jump up and down and pump on your chest to try to bring you back to life?"

He looked confused but he answered quickly, "What are you asking me? I have a book to finish," he said. "I never said I wanted to die."

"Wrong answer," I said, reaching for the phone. Once you tell me you want to live, and that you want me to jump on your chest and breathe for you when you fall over, that's something else. Now that I know what you want, I would be an idiot to try heroics here. You need the best medical care we can get you. So now we call Lanetta and fly to California."

After I talked to Lanetta and asked her to make us plane reservations as soon as she could, I gave Mario another Lasix and another Valium. Then I called the front desk and ordered a wheel chair so he wouldn't have to walk.

But Mario hated that idea. "I'm not sitting in this chair while you push me through the airport," he insisted. "Everyone will think I'm dying."

I didn't want to fight but time was essential. "Okay," I said. "God forbid anyone thinks you're really sick." I ran into the bedroom, rifled through my suitcase and found an ace bandage. Then I ran back to Mario, and told him, "Lift your foot, either one."

"What are you doing?" he asked me.

"I'm wrapping your ankle," I said. "That's what I'm doing."

"But you said it was my heart," he said.

"Look, make up your mind," I said. "Do you want people to think you're dying or that you have a sprained ankle?"

He laughed. "You are a wonder, my girl," he said. "A true wonder."

Chapter 36

When we arrived at the gate in LA, Lanetta was waiting.

As the airline steward pushed Mario's wheelchair down the ramp, she came running toward us. "What happened?" she asked, pointing to his leg.

"Nothing," I explained. "It's a disguise."

She wrapped her arms around Mario's neck. "Oh Boss," she said. "I'm so happy to see you." Then she smiled at me and said, "We have a doctor's appointment with the best doctors in town. But first I promised Dr. Mac that I would bring Mario by for a quick checkup."

"Great," I said, but Mario was not smiling.

"Mario, stop looking so sullen," I said laughing. "We might have just stopped you from being dead."

He looked up without expression. "We're not in the clear yet," he said.

"True," I said, "I'm just playing the odds."

Once Dr. Mac examined Mario, he immediately called the best cardiology group in Beverly Hills to make an appointment for the following day.

I was so relieved that Lanetta was there with us because she always made hard things easier. She had already called Mario's kids to fly to LA. I was glad that they were on their way; they would be great support for both of us. I had no official title in relationship to Mario, so I couldn't sign any of the medical consents for any of his treatments. That always made me furious, but the boys would make sure to include me.

Dr. Mac was a tall grey haired experienced doctor, and right now he looked serious. After listening to Mario's heart, he told Mario there could be no procrastinating. When he turned to Lanetta and me, he said, "If there is any problem, take him to Cedar's Sinai ER immediately."

He handed me a sample of a calcium channel blocker and said, "Start him on these right away."

I looked at the box and knew Mario had a really bad reaction to it before. I tried to explain it to Dr. Mac, but he didn't seem to hear. When Mario reached out and put his hand on my arm to stop me from "arguing," I stopped. Once outside, I threw the pills in my bag and thought, "Nope, I'm not giving him even one pill—not until we're somewhere where they have a crash cart."

That night in Malibu was the roughest night I ever spent. Mario was gurgling and getting bluer by the minute and still refused to have me call an ambulance to take him into the hospital. He kept insisting he could wait until morning. There were mudslides along Pacific Coast highway and he said he didn't want to take the chance on getting caught in one. About 3 in the morning, before I could stop him, he took 3 valium and knocked himself out.

Until dawn broke, I sat up in bed next to him watching him struggle to breathe, not being able to tell the kids or Lanetta because he'd made me promise I wouldn't. "No sense worrying everyone," he said, "There will be plenty of time for sleepless nights if I have to have anything done."

"What about me?" I asked. "I would like the company and to be able to share the responsibility."

"Okay," he said, "I'll share the responsibility with you. Toughen up, honey, you can take it, you're a nurse. Let the kids and Lanetta sleep."

Mario did keep breathing, though badly, till morning when Lanetta arrived to drive us to the specialist.

The three doctors who made up the cardiology group in Beverly Hills had no medical records or history for Mario, so I had to give the details over and over again. Finally, the youngest of the partners, a Doctor Allen, came to speak with me.

"I'd like to do a Thalium stress test," he said. "I think that's our best chance of non-invasive test for diagnosis."

"Okay," I said, "but his pulse is very erratic. Every time we give a new medication, his blood pressure tanks. Besides, last night his breathing was lousy. I'm not doing that again."

"Okay," Dr. Allen said, as politely as only LA doctors can, "I'll schedule the Thalium study right away."

Mario's three sons and Lanetta went with Mario for the Thalium study. His daughter, Virginia and I were driving back to Malibu to pick up some of his clothes and grab something for dinner.

But we only made it as far as Santa Monica before the phone rang. It was Dr. Allen. "I don't like what I see. Several of his arteries are blocked. I can't take the chance he'll have a heart attack with you all the way out in Malibu."

"Okay," I said. "Admit him."

"He's refusing to go, or sign any consents for tests or treatment until he speaks to you," he said.

"We'll be right there," I said. "Tell him to sign the consents."

"I have to admit him to the hospital," the doctor said, "I want to do an angiogram as soon as I can schedule it."

Doctor Allen met us at the hospital. "We put him in a private room on the cardiac floor so we could watch him until we see more clearly what we're dealing with. Follow me up, I've got some orders to write."

We stopped at the Nurses Station and then walked down to the end of the hall to Mario's room.

Mario was just sitting in bed reading. The boys were sitting in the chairs across the room and Lanetta was sitting in a chair right next to him.

"Well, here I am in your old stomping grounds," he said, looking up at me, "and I must admit, it does make me feel safer being in a hospital."

I frowned. "Foolish man," I teased him.

"Comes from when I was a kid and they put me in the hospital for Rheumatic Fever," he said. "I had all kinds of books and games to play and different foods every day. I was there for months."

"You liked the hospital food?" I asked.

"I did," he said. "All except for Fridays when we had fish."

"You were in a Catholic Hospital?" I asked.

"I was," he said. "But nobody bothered me. Nobody asked me to pray. All I had to do was lay around all day and read."

We all visited Mario for a while and when the dietician came in to discuss his menu, he lit up like a kid.

"I think maybe Virginia and I should try to go back out to the house again and pick up some comfortable clothes for you," I told him, "We'll be back for visiting hours, later."

"Sure," he said. "But you should all go out and have a nice dinner tonight."

"Can't do it," I said. "It's not the same without you."

We barely had time to get to the house and relax before Dr. Allen called again and told us to come back to the hospital.

Now standing at the nursing station at Cedar's, the doctor confessed, "No sooner did we start the damn drip than his heart started throwing PVC's and we spent the rest of the time trying to stabilize him. We have to transfer him to the Cardiac Intensive Care Unit to stabilize him so we can keep a closer eye on his monitor."

"Okay," I said, relieved. I was just glad I never gave him the sample pills Dr. Mac had given me the day before. At least now he was already in the hospital.

On the way to Mario's new room Virginia and I had to pass the large antechamber where Dorothy, Mario's oldest daughter, a director, and the boys were sitting waiting. Lanetta had gone home to take care of her family after spending all day at the hospital.

Tony said, "Something happened."

Dr. Allen told us he had called in the best cardiac surgeon and spoken to him already—Dr. Silverberg. He was certain that they would have to do several bypasses. Then he pointed to the end of the hall. "It's the last room to the left. It's one of our best VIP rooms and the biggest so all of you can visit. But only one of you can stay overnight."

Mario's youngest son, Joey, volunteered.

When we got to Mario's room, I was amazed. It was better than some of the 5 star hotels Mario and I had stayed in. There were couches and lounge chairs in it, and plenty of space. There was an IV dripping slowly into Mario's left arm. He was sitting up in bed, rails up, holding a paperback book that he had been reading.

We all walked in together. When Mario saw us he straightened up and tried to look regal. Before any of us had a chance to speak, he announced, "To you my eldest son, Anthony, I give the lands belonging to the British Empire. To you, my son Eugene, next in line, I give the entire Roman Empire. To you my eldest daughter, Dorothy, I give the kingdoms of the Turkish empire, and to you, my daughter, Virginia, I give the Caribbean Islands, with it's vast beaches and beautiful mountains and to you, my youngest son, Joseph, I bequeath the Ottoman Empire." Then he turned to me. "Ah, and to you my love, I give the ancient empire of Egypt and all its wealth and holdings. Rule them well."

"Mario," I said, frowning, "You're mixing up your timeline and your empires. But really, why did you let them give you that medicine? We just talked about it yesterday. Now your doctor said your heart almost stopped."

"Yes, my dear, that is true. But there are other considerations. He is the doctor after all, and I am sleeping under his roof and taking advantage of his hospitality. I must show him some respect."

The kids all gathered round him, relieved that he sounded okay. Virginia and Joey held his hands and both of the older boys stood at the bottom of the bed. His daughter Dorothy stood by the door so as not to disturb his monitor leads or his IV.

"The doctor said you have to have an angiogram," I told him, "so they can get a clearer view of your arteries, and check out the condition of your heart muscle to determine if there's been any damage to your heart."

"Is it painful?" he asked.

"It's not a picnic," I explained. "But I have had patients who felt almost nothing and others who swore it felt like a grenade exploding in their chest. You'll probably feel something but they seem to have a pretty good staff here so they can help manage your discomfort."

We were there less than an hour when a nurse showed up in the room to tell us that Mario had to be prepped for the angiogram. A Dr. Silverberg, the cardiac surgeon, had managed to get everyone together to do it.

It seemed like only minutes before Mario was on a stretcher to go down to the cath lab for his angiogram. He smiled at us, "Carry on," he said to all of us.

"Remember" I said, leaning down to kiss him, "Keep an eye out for a vision."

Chapter 37

We all went into the waiting room to sit. We chatted to each other, but each of us was preoccupied and concerned about Mario. Tony asked what we could expect, and what the outcome would tell us. "I guess it depends on whether they're going to do a double or triple bypass, and how good the heart muscle is," I said, trying to reassure.

We made small talk, but still it seemed to take hours before we learned anything. Finally, Dr. Allen came out into the waiting room. "It went well," he said. Then he offered to allow me into the recovery room to wait for Mario to wake up.

"What's the verdict?" I asked him.

"Looks like it's going to be at least a triple bypass," he said. "maybe a quadruple. The LDA, the main heart artery is almost completely blocked."

Mario was lying on a stretcher still out cold when I saw him but he looked pretty good. Still, he wasn't awake. But as soon as he opened his eyes and began to stir, the nurse was right there to move his stretcher out of recovery and back to his room.

I followed the stretcher while the kids stayed in the waiting room.

As two nurses wheeled Mario out of the recovery room, I ran alongside the stretcher trying to keep up. He was still groggy from the anesthesia, and I wanted to be sure he was okay. His eyes were closed but his color was good.

"Mario," I whispered, as the stretcher slowed down at the elevator, "Mario, it's me. It's Carol. Are you awake?"

"Shh...shh," he whispered back. "I'm not ready to wake up yet."

"Are you okay?" I asked again. "Was it awful for you? Are you in pain?"

One young nurse looked over at me and smiled a reassurance. "He did very well," she said, as the elevator door opened.

I squeezed into the elevator with them.

Later, back in bed in his own room, still not fully awake, he smiled again and struggled to open his eyes.

Hovering over him, smoothing his hair from his forehead, I asked softly. "Did you see anything, did you hear anything? Do you remember?"

"Remember?" he asked, his voice still thick with anesthesia.

"You know like the Near Death Experiences we talked about before you went in?" He opened his eyes and looked at me, expressionless.

"I did my dear," Mario said. "I really did. Be patient."

"Tell me," I said, holding my breath. I had heard so many amazing stories from patients I had taken care of over the years, and they always reassured me.

"It was incredible," Mario said slowly, but then he hesitated.

"It's okay, honey," I said. "Tell me. Tell me what you saw." I was holding his hand to reassure him.

Mario began, "I was in the middle of the clearest sky—a sky so blue it was like nothing I've ever seen—and below me I saw mountains and mountains of fluffy white." He hesitated and took a deep breath. Then his eyes closed and he seemed to doze off again.

I waited as long as I could before I whispered, "Mario, Mario? You were telling me about your vision. You saw fluffy..."

His eyes opened again. "Yes, yes," he said, "fluffy white mashed potatoes swimming in lakes of rich brown gravy and," he took a deep breath. "Flying overhead like hundreds of dark birds, there was an enormous flock of chipped beef just like we had in the army mess hall. It seemed so real."

I didn't know whether to laugh or not. "You're kidding right? Chipped beef and mashed potatoes covered in gravy is your idea of heaven? That's your idea of a vision?"

I tried not to sound disappointed but I was hoping for a big heavenly vision, some kind of glimpse into the worlds after life.

"No, it wasn't my idea of heaven. I don't believe in heaven," Mario said. "But, remembering it brought me right back to earth."

Dr. Silverberg was going to do Mario's surgery first thing in the morning. "You can all go home and get some rest tonight," he told us. "There will be plenty of time to spend with him when he needs you after surgery."

But the boys decided they would stay anyway, in case Mario got terrified.

Mario was still cheerful when we saw him the following morning, and while the boys went home to shower and change their clothes, Virginia, Lanetta and I spent some hours chatting with him. Dorothy came to visit for a while and when the boys returned, Virginia and I went out for lunch. But we hadn't even made it to Santa Monica, before we got a call from Dr. Allen. "Get back here and make him sign these papers," he said. "We have no time to waste."

What happened? I asked. But he'd hung up.

By the time we got back, Mario had been moved to a small Cardiac Intensive Care Unit with only a few other patients in cubicles, curtains drawn so we couldnt see them.

Mario lay in bed looking pale and listless

"What happened? We just left you a few hours ago," I said, pulling the small metal chair close to the bed. I sat down and reached for his hand. "Don't dare try and die when I'm not around," I said.

"They gave me more medicine," he told me. "But my heart kept acting funny. So, it was good we came here. You were right again." He smiled. "Well, Butch," he said. "Fine fix you got us into this time..."

"Me?" I said. "It's your heart."

"Well, what do we do now, doc?" he asked.

"Dr. Silverberg said he's got to take you upstairs for surgery. Probably a triple bypass," I told him. "Has he talked to you yet?"

"Yes, he said something about that when he asked me to sign those papers. Sorry, I couldn't wait for you but he said if I waited any longer I could die, and I didn't think you'd want that either."

"Very true," I said. "So now we're just waiting for what?" I asked.

There was only one nurse overseeing the unit, and so I walked over to her and asked, "What's going on? Do you have any idea when Mario's going up for surgery?"

She was sharp looking and pleasant. "There was an emergency surgery," she said. "We're just waiting for everyone to come back. Then we'll call the OR to send a stretcher."

In the background I could hear Mario's monitor, beeping erratically. I turned to see several irregular beats—PVC's—coming close together. Bad sign.

I walked back over to him. "What are you doing?" I asked pointing at the monitor.

"I feel kind of funny," he admitted.

"Don't even think about dying on me," I said. "Or I won't forgive you. Ever."

He smiled at me, but his eyes were beginning to close. He was losing consciousness. I shook his shoulder. "Mario. Do you have your wallet?" I asked.

His eyes shot open and he looked at me puzzled. "My wallet?" he repeated. "It's in the drawer."

"Good," I said.

"Why?" he asked, and his voice was weak.

"Insurance," I said.

I reached into the drawer in his bedside stand and pulled out his wallet. As he watched me, I took out his American Express Card and showed it to him.

Then, I put it in my pocket. "Okay," I told him. "This is the deal. If you die, before anyone has a chance to stop me, I'll take this card, run up and down both sides of Rodeo drive and rack up so many charges that your kids will have half the inheritance you want them to. You live through that surgery and the first thing I do is give it back to you. That's the deal."

He rolled his eyes and laughed. "You're a pretty good shopper," he said, weakly. "A threat like that from anyone else would mean nothing, but from you..." He laughed again and I could hear gurgling as he breathed. I looked up at the monitor just as he threw several more PVC's. Any minute now he would go into V-TAC which could be fatal.

"Deal," he said, just before he lost consciousness.

"Nurse," I called.

She was on the phone, and she was watching the monitor. She saw just what I did. "It's the OR," she called back to me. "They're sending down a stretcher."

"They'd better hurry," I said.

The nurse quickly rolled over the portable monitor and hooked Mario's leads up.

Mario's heart was beating even more erratically. "We don't have time to wait for a stretcher," she said. "We're going to have to take the bed."

She ran over to the door of the unit and called down the hall for another nurse to watch the unit. Then she rushed back over to the bed. "He's in trouble," she said, "Let's move him fast."

"Sure," I said. "Which way to the OR?"

She was talking as she put the portable oxygen on him and threw the small tank on the bed alongside the monitor. The EKG tape now looked like a series of very large mountains—a mountain range in fact.

She said, "You take one side, I'll take the other. It will keep the bed straight as we push through the door."

We began to push hard until we reached the hall. I looked down the long corridor, and then I looked at Mario whose eyelids were now fluttering.

"Don't you dare," I said. "Don't even think about it. Remember, I have your credit card."

Mario nodded. But the nurse looked at me as though I was crazy.

Mario was getting paler and his breathing was more labored as we rushed down the hall.

"The elevator," the nurse said, pointing down the corridor.

When we reached the elevators, she pushed the button frantically. Once, twice, and on the third time the door opened. Empty. No stretcher, no OR staff.

"We'll have to take him ourselves," I said. "We don't have time."

She nodded. "Okay. Push," she said.

"Did you bring the ambu—bag," I asked. "In case?"

She nodded.

"Mario?" I called. But his eyes were shut. "Mario?" I called again, but there was no response. "Damn," I said.

She said, "He's out."

Just as she said it, the monitor showed V-TAC. "We're losing him," she said.

"Mario?" I threatened. "Don't you dare!!"

The elevator stopped and the doors opened outside the OR. Mario stopped breathing and the monitor began a high pitched insistent beep. The screen showed a straight line.

Suddenly the OR doors opened. Several orderlies and nurses poured out and grabbed the bed away from us, and I saw Dr. Silverberg, his mask on, his gloved hands up in the air. As the Operating Room doors swung shut, beneath my breath I whispered, "Please Mario, don't die on me. Not now. Not even for a vision." I took a deep breath. I knew that OR staff had only a minute or two to bring him back. Now I was praying. "Remember," I said aloud again, "I have your credit card."

That's when I started to cry.

Chapter 38

It seemed like hours before we heard anything.

We all sat together in the waiting room, but each of us spent time thinking, sitting, standing, and pacing up and down. Every now and then we'd say something to each other, but not much. To pass the time, we made up a schedule so that each of us could stay in the hospital with Mario to make sure someone would always be there.

My biggest concern, aside from his survival, was that Mario hadn't gotten enough oxygen and might have some brain damage. Even subtle damage could cause him not be able to concentrate enough on his writing to do what he wanted. That would be deadly because if Mario couldn't write, he would no longer want to live. That was it.

Finally after more hours than I thought I could bear, Dr. Silverberg, came out into the waiting room to talk to us. "He did well. Quadruple bypass. He's still out but we'll keep him in CCU for the night and they'll try to wean him off the respirator. Once he can breathe on his own, we're almost home free."

The Recovery Rooms for the Cardiac ICU in Cedars-Sinai Hospital were small curtained cubicles. When we finally saw Mario, he still wasn't conscious. He was on the respirator and the only sound in the room was the regular beeping of the heart monitor and the hissing of that respirator. Mario's color was good, much better than the last time I'd seen him.

The kids and I spent the whole day waiting for Mario regain consciousness, but he didn't wake up, even late into the evening. Though his vital signs were good, and the staff assured us nothing was wrong, he just wouldn't open his eyes no matter who spoke to him.

When we left to go home, his eyes were still shut. The nurses said they'd try to take him off the respirator sometime during the night. So while we all went home to sleep, Joey stayed overnight to stand guard. None of us wanted to leave him but we were all dead exhausted and wanted to be sure he would see familiar faces when he finally regained consciousness.

The following morning, we all got there early. Joey told us that Mario wasn't on the respirator any longer, and had even nodded once or twice when he asked him a question but no words yet.

Because the cubicle in the CCU was so small, only one of us could go in at a time.

Lanetta was already there with him when I pushed the curtains back and walked in. She was whispering to him, encouraging him to wake up.

Mario was propped up in bed with an IV running but I didn't know how alert he was yet. The monitor was beeping regularly in the background. His color was good but his eyes were still closed.

"Boss?" Lanetta said. "Boss, it's La..." But he said nothing.

I tried to speak to him and then, one by one, so did the kids. Still by noon, he was barely moving.

Dr. Allen told us to go out to get something to eat and maybe by the time we got back, he'd be awake.

We went reluctantly. But two of the kids stayed just in case.

By the time we got back it had been so many hours since he had gotten out of surgery they we were all exhausted just from worrying. Though the doctors and nurses had gotten him off the respirator so he could breathe on his own, no one had heard him speak yet.

Finally I walked over to the bed next to him and grabbed his hand, squeezing it tight. I kissed his cheek, his skin was warm and dry. Good.

"Mario, Mario," I whispered, "It's over. You're okay. How do you feel?"

He nodded his head but kept his eyes closed.

"Can you hear me?" I asked him, my voice a little louder. He turned toward me, eyes still closed and nodded again.

I was thrilled that he was conscious but still concerned because I didn't know if he had lost any brain cells. He would hate that, even if I could deal with it. His writing was the only thing he said he lived for....

I squeezed his hand. "Mario," I said, "Can you speak?"

He smiled, but still hadn't opened his eyes. I could almost feel my heart beating in my chest. "Mario," I said, moving up closer to him. "You have to speak to me, so I'm sure you're okay."

He nodded and whispered, "Hi Honey." His voice was strong enough, no slur, but I still wasn't reassured. I mean almost anyone could be "honey." Lanetta, Virginia, or anyone else he was fond of.

My anxiety was making the hair on the back of my neck stand on end.

When I had last seen Mario, his heart had stopped and we had just rolled him into the Operating Room. I didn't know how long it was before his heart started beating again, or if he had suffered any loss of oxygen that could destroy brain cells. If Mario couldn't think, he couldn't write; if he couldn't write, he wouldn't want to live; if he didn't want to live, he could will himself dead and his whole family would be devastated. Not to speak about how I would feel.

So I decided just to lay it on the line and give it to him straight. "Mario," I whispered, "I know it looks like you're okay, your color is good, and I know that you can speak, but I don't know if you have lost any of your powers. So I need you to say something that will let me know that you're still in there, and that healing your heart didn't wreck your brain, or your ability to think and write. I need to know if you know who I am."

Now, his eyes shot open and he looked right into mine. He raised his eyebrows, then he motioned me to come closer. When I did, he whispered in my ear.

I burst out laughing and I kissed him hard before I went running out of the booth to tell the kids and Lanetta, "He's good, he's fine and he has all his marbles. He can talk and he can think."

"How do you know? What did he say?" Tony asked.

"*Give me back my credit card*," I said, and then we all laughed and began to breathe again.

Chapter 39

After the surgery, Mario had to slow down his adventurous life, so all his travel plans were now put on hold. I was perfectly fine with that, especially because we could spend time together at home having long conversations about books and ideas behind them. He wrote some of his philosophy in the book "The Fortunate Pilgrim," one of the best books I've ever read about a heroic woman. But that was many years before.

It was another of the evenings when we were sitting in the study after dinner talking. I asked, "So, what do you see now from the vantage point of age? What is the difference between you when you wrote the book at 41 years old and you now?"

He hesitated before he said, "Honey, all I can tell you is that was nothing I thought of consciously while I was writing the book. Then I was trying to tell the story of this heroic young boy who wanted something more than life in the slums. But, when I read it, I knew it was a story about my mother."

"What about it made it her story?" I asked.

"She was the most heroic," he said. "She stood up to adversity. One of her husband's got killed, one was in an asylum, she had children who wouldn't obey her and yet she held it all together out of sheer belief in Life."

"What kind of belief in Life?" I asked him.

"Those old women had their duty to their family," he said, and he made it sound as important as patriotism in wartime. "With those Italian women, their loyalty never went beyond their families."

"That duty to their family was survival?" I asked.

"Survival and the keeping of the dream to lead a decent life," he said. He lit his cigar, and leaned back remembering. "Trouble was my mother and most of those women had no sympathy for anyone else's dreams," he said.

"What do you see as her greatest strength?" I asked him.

He didn't say a word as he thought about it. Finally, he said, "Her greatest strength was that she stayed engaged in life. She held tight to the belief that Life itself was worthwhile."

I asked. "What kept her hope alive?"

"I believe it was adversity," he said. "She grew up on a farm in Italy. At ten years old she was cooking for all the farm workers, she had no prospects, she traveled to America to marry a man who she hadn't seen since they were children together. She took all these gambles."

"So she was a big risk taker," I said.

"She was ruthless," he said.

"In what way?" I asked.

"Well, she made decisions that were ruthless," he said. "Like when she thinks about her first husband dying, she thinks it was all for the best. You know, she was like you. You're like one of those old Italian women too. When she has to make the decision to take her husband out of the mental hospital, she decides not to take him."

"What do you think her rationale was?" I asked him.

"She knew it would destroy the family. So better to sacrifice him than sacrifice the family," he said. "She had to make those terrible decisions."

I asked him, "Does that quality exist in both women and men?"

Mario said, "That was a world that existed thousands of years ago."

"What do you mean?" I asked.

"I mean women aren't the same today," he said. "Men aren't the same today."

"I thought you just said I was like one of those old Italian women."

"You're an exception," he said.

"I don't agree with you on that one. I know a lot of women like me," I said. "That's what makes the character of your mother in that book timeless. But what I was asking was whether you thought those qualities exist more in women than in men. Or is the change in society what makes those qualities less valuable now?"

Mario pulled out a cigar, and began to chew on it. "You have to remember that my mother was a comparatively young woman when she condemned herself to live without a male for the rest of her life. She did that at great personal sacrifice," he explained. "But the world has changed so much that it's like an antique world."

I said, "What your mother knew then is what women are growing into now." I stopped and thought about it. Then I asked, "So do you think these traits...

"So do you think these traits are female or are they traits of character that belong to heads of organizations or families?"

"I think they're women's traits," he said.

"What's the difference in the way men make decisions?" I asked.

"If the situation had been reversed, a man would have taken his wife out of the mental institution," he said. "He would have gambled that everything would have been okay. He would have taken a shot."

"To what end?"

"Well, to have his mate back for companionship—and to do his duty and bring his wife back," he said. "Maybe he doesn't have the vision to see what can happen to a family," he said.

"Where do you think that comes from?" I asked.

"When a man marries a woman he becomes responsible for her," he said. "But part of the pride of possession, is that he can protect her."

"So being a husband forces a man who doesn't want to look bad to choose his wife first?" I asked. "But a woman..."

Mario interrupted me. "...is more ruthless."

"She is also more connected to her children," I said. "Because primarily she feels responsible for them." Now I was confused. "If that's how you feel, how did the women in The Godfather and the other books except for the last ones get to look like so much fluff? Why did you let those macho guys take over so much?"

Mario was frowning. He was thinking hard.

So I went on. "I mean Kay was nothing to Michael. Sonny's wife was nothing as a character. Even The Godfather's wife was invisible."

Mario came alive. "Yes, but now you're talking about terribly ambitious men— tremendously ego driven men who wanted power in the outside world."

"Go on," I said.

"Well, in The Godfather and The Sicilian I was writing on the grand scale of history. They're different kinds of books. They're epic books. The Fortunate Pilgrim is a very intimate portrait of ordinary life."

"But your mother was an extraordinary woman," I said. "Is that what made her a hero?"

"In the culture of The Sicilian and The Godfather, women were not important. They didn't have any voice."

"How can that be if you say you were writing about an Italian family?" I asked.

"Their problems were not the problems of the Fortunate Pilgrim. The men in my other books had macho problems of physical power and murder. In that world, men had to respond with force," he explained.

"So your saying a male hero has a different job?" I asked. "He has more to do with protection and destruction?"

"In the outside world," he said.

"A woman's heroism comes from?" I asked.

"The minute disasters of everyday living," he said. "Women in everyday life operate *within* the structure of society. Within that structure of society, they encounter terrible tragedies that they can handle. Men, on the other hand, in my books, are breaking down the structure of society. They're doing a different thing."

"I don't get that," I said. "Your mother who had her husband locked up worked and lived within society?"

"She made a decision that society didn't approve of, but she didn't break down the structure. There was disapproval of her actions, but it still was within society. What I'm saying is that women can cope better with the tragedies of everyday life."

"Are they smaller tragedies?" I asked.

"No," he said quickly. "But they're different tragedies. Men can cope with something they can struggle with: Outside forces. But they're not good with the inside things that happen. Like you can take a very heroic man who can stand up to society, commit murder and yet a little thing like getting older happens that can throw him like it never would a woman."

Suddenly, Mario looked puzzled. "You know, the more I think about it, the things the Godfather says and does are pretty much what my mother said and did."

"So then The Godfather was closest to your mother?" I said, laughing. "That's funny."

"It's nothing I ever thought of consciously,' Mario said. "But the truth is, that every time the Godfather speaks...I do hear the voice of my mother."

I didn't tease him then. I could see in his eyes what he felt. For me, I knew that he really understood the battle his mother had fought. The battle all women fight.

"Thank you," I said.

"Thank you," he said. "Until now, I really didn't get it."

Then I asked, "So what hope is there for humanity? That's my real question."

Mario picked up his cigar and began to chew on it, his eyes ticking his thoughts. Then he was soft and serious when he said, "Stop fighting for equality for women, they've already got an edge. Treat everyone with respect: man or woman. Each of us must have less self interest and all of us must become more virtuous or there is no hope for evolution. Self-interest will take us all down."

"That's what you were trying to say in The Godfather?" I asked.

"That's what I'm saying now," he said. "That book was all about American Business, about greed and the fight for power–about the importance of family, and even more about the dangers of capitalism."

Chapter 40

It wasn't always heaven. In fact, sometimes it was really hard. Mario and I were such different people that we never quite made a WE. We made an I+I. The thing is that as we were learning about each other, we were learning about ourselves. The truth was that over time each of us made the other better.

On this weekend, Mario did nothing different from usual. I mean he didn't attack, he didn't incite, he didn't even talk. He just sat and stared out the window, watched TV or read. I, of course, was on my computer again writing and typing both his manuscript and mine for most of the day.

Mario loved stories. He often said that I was his Scheherazade: the princess from Arabian Nights. When I admitted I hadn't read about her, he explained. "There once was a Persian king whose wife had been unfaithful to him. So he vowed that he would marry a new wife each day, a virgin, and slay her the following morning in order to marry another. He would do that for 1000 days. Against her father's wishes, Scheherazade offered herself to the king one night. But she had planted her sister to ask her to tell a story.

"Scheherazade began her story and told it long into the night. But by dawn she had not finished it, and so the king asked her to come back the following night. That night, when her story ended, she quickly began to tell another even more exciting story.

For 1001 nights she told the king stories, and when each story ended, she began another. By the time Scheherazade confessed to the king that she had no more tales to tell him, he had already fallen in love with her. So, he spared her life, and made her his queen."

"So we're good as long as I tell stories," I said to Mario, laughing.

"I'm convinced that most marriages fall apart because there's nothing left to say."

Because I was a nurse, I always had stories to tell, stories that dealt with things that were interesting to Mario, and so he loved to hear what was going on with all of my nurse friends.

He was fascinated by how others' thought, especially women. So usually after we wound down from a day of work, he loved to sit on the couch with me, chat and hear about my friends. Often, I'd share tidbits of some conversations because he knew each of them.

On this night I started with, "Hey, guess what? My friends took a vote and they said they trust me more than anyone else."

Mario, who was still sitting in his leather chair with his feet up on his desk, reading, said, "Well, I trust you in some things too. I can understand that."

Suddenly, instantly, I was a crazed person. "What do you mean in *some things*?"

He frowned and looked up, surprised. "Well, I'd trust you to save my life," he said.

"Okay. That's sort of a big thing. What is it you don't trust me with?"

Mario looked confused. "There are some things I trust the boys with more."

I knew he wasn't being mean, so I asked him, "Is there anything you've ever asked for that I haven't done? Has there ever been a time that you needed something that I wasn't there?"

He put his book down and stared at me, assessing me. "Well," he said, softly, "You're unpredictable sometimes."

"Unpredictable?" I said, keeping my voice low. "I have been so damn predictable that I even bore myself sometimes." As an example, I said, "Every year or so don't I struggle with you about not being married?" I took a deep breath. "Don't I tell you how dangerous and difficult it is if you get sick? If we're away I have no legal standing and can't make decisions for you in an emergency?"

He nodded and then frowned. He was thinking. It took so long for him to speak that I knew I'd grow old until the words that were flying around his brain fell from his lips. I couldn't tell whether he was going to stay silent and just hold it against me, or take the chance and speak.

"Would you please tell me what you're thinking?" I asked, carefully.

He looked at me. Just looked. No expression except maybe, caution. He took a deep breath and said, "You keep telling me to talk to you, then you get upset. That's why I keep quiet."

"But listen to what you're saying," I tell him. "How do you expect me to react when after 18 years of doing everything you want me too, you still don't trust me?"

He said, "I do trust you in most things. I said I trust you with my life. That's something."

"You trust your doctors too," I said. "And a few of them are not even worth trusting. That's not the kind of trust I'm talking about. I'm not talking about a professional trust because I'm an ace diagnostician. I'm talking about a personal trust."

"I don't trust anyone one hundred percent," he tried to explain. "I don't trust anyone more than I trust myself."

"Well, of course not," I said. "I don't expect that. I trust myself more than anyone else too. But still, even after all the promises you made and broke, I still trust you."

Mario got quiet again, but I could see a lot was going on behind his eyes. He felt reproached. His fingers moved as though he was explaining something.

"If you think you're speaking," I said, "I want you to know I can't hear you. Not a word has passed your lips."

He suddenly looked sad. "I'm trying to think of what to say," he explained.

Suddenly, I felt awful. I didn't want to make him feel bad. I just wanted to know what I had done so I could fix it.

"What do you feel I've been trying to tell you?" I asked.

He sat up straight and said, "You want to be married. I've made you unhappy, and I have to try harder."

In that moment, there wasn't a prayer in any religion that could be said to make me want to be married. But I really didn't want to fight with him, and so I said, "I'm not unhappy. I'm just devastated that you don't trust me after all this time. Besides, I'm only devastated for now. As soon as I work this out, I'll be fine. I just don't understand."

I got a Coke out of the refrigerator, and gave it to him. Then I pulled up a chair close to his, and asked him in a really quiet voice, "What the hell are you going to try harder at? Trusting me?" Mario looked so stricken, I quickly said, "Okay, I mean I know you trust me with your life, but what don't you trust me with? Why don't you trust me 100%? I just want to understand."

"Only the boys know my finances," he explained, "No one else does. You and I are partners. You know more about me than anyone else ever has."

"Partners?" I said, and then I just shook my head. "But you're like a partner with a second set of books." I took a deep breath. "By now you have to know I don't want your money. I've offered a thousand times to sign any kind of papers you had drawn up..."

He looked at me and smiled affectionately, but I was busy imagining him growing hate plants in his heart. "I couldn't love anyone who I had to make sign papers," he said.

"Then I want to know why you don't trust me," I repeated. "That's all. I am just trying to understand."

"I can't explain it," he said. "It's a *feeling*."

"Can you try to put that feeling into words?" I asked. "Is it the Italian thing? Like I'm not the woman who bore your children? Or is it because I'm smart? Or is it because no matter how long we go out, and how much we love each other, I'm still on the outside of the family because the same blood doesn't course through my veins and yours?"

Mario thought about it for a long time. I forced myself to sit in the smothering silence, for as long as I could without saying anything. I felt hurt and then tried to talk myself out of feeling hurt, because I knew he didn't mean to hurt me. But it was always really hard for me to let go of something that broke my heart until I could understand it.

Instead, I sat silently and tried not to stare at him. I tried not to look like he'd committed some terrible crime and I was the District Attorney. I even asked myself how I could expect him to feel safe enough to speak when I was sitting in a chair so close to him, waiting for an answer. I knew I wouldn't speak to anyone who was grilling me. But Mario is kind. He finally comes across. He's braver than me. Or he figured, *what the hell?*

"Well," he began, "You are smart. That's a help sometimes and other times, you're a little too smart. I know that whatever I say, you'll use your own judgment." When I frowned, trying to understand, he continued, "If I ask the boys to do something, they do it. They won't make up their own minds about what's good and what's not."

"This is a good thing?" I asked.

"Well, they'll do what I want," he said, "whether it's a good thing or not."

I shook my head because in a funny way it made sense.

Then he added, "Please stop saying I don't trust you because you're on the outside of the family. That's not it. I don't trust my daughters any more than I trust you."

"Oh my God," I said, covering my face and almost falling off the chair. "You mean this is a gender thing? You mean this is because I'm a *woman*?"

"Look," Mario said. "Try to understand what I'm saying. To be a success, I had the boys around me, to drive me, to keep my books, to keep everyone away so I could write."

"I get that," I said. "And I know they help me too. But you keep saying how great women are, and yet now you sound like the old way is the best way? The boys? What is this really about? I thought you were a Renaissance man."

"You want the truth?" he asked.

"Of course," I said.

"I can't help how I feel," he said. "I told you I couldn't marry you because, right or wrong, this is a Patriarchy, and there's no room in a Patriarchy for a woman like you. I asked you if you wanted to give up your writing and cook for me. You said no. You'd hate living like that. You'd leave me. But before you did, you'd cause the collapse of my whole organization. The wives of my sons would begin to rebel. You'd even have my daughters getting discontent."

I got his point but still I was heartsick. I marched for feminism in the sixties, I believed in women's rights always. Intellectually, I knew women didn't get a fair shake much of the time. But until that very moment, I never *felt* discriminated against personally, just because I was female. Now, I was really sick about it. How did I do this to myself? How after all my struggling did I wind up in this position? I was neither fish nor fowl. Too independent for a woman, too smart, but never, no matter how hard I tried, would or could I ever be a man? I felt the sharp pain of mortal defeat. I wanted to be a woman, to live and love as a woman, but I wanted the rights they gave men!! Shit!!

"Et tu, Brute?" I said to Mario. Then without another word, I walked into the bathroom to cry.

"Think about it, please honey?" he said. "I can't change the rules in the middle of the game. The boys had their jobs, their positions and they stuck by me at their own personal expense. After all those years, how can I change the game now? How is that fair?"

"It's not," I said. "It's just crummy."

"See why I don't talk?" I could hear him saying through the door. "It doesn't pay."

Through both the door and my tears and sniffling nose, I told him, "You know, underneath, I'm kinder than I sound. And underneath, you're a lot less kind than you sound."

"Write that down," he said. "And write a book that works. Then we can be equals."

I got really mad. "You know Mario, the flip side of your humility is real arrogance."

Through the door he said, "But honey, the flip side of your arrogance is....just...more arrogance."

I started to laugh. "That was funny," I said, as I opened the door. "I mean, even though it was insulting, it was funny."

"Come here," he said, and put his arms around me, "I can't help how I feel. It's who I am. A man of a certain generation. My mind knows it's not fair. And I do love you. Just write your books and you'll feel better."

"I hate that you think men are better than women," I told him.

He looked surprised. "I don't," he said. "Actually, I believe women are better than men, I told you that before. All I said was I didn't trust them as much."

I gave it up. I stopped talking to him about it. I let it go.

Then just before we fell asleep, lying in bed next to each other, he said, "Why do you take everything I say, even when it's just off the top of my head, to heart. I was just talking."

"Does that mean that you do trust women the same as men?" I asked.

In the dark I couldn't see his face, but what he said was, "No, what I meant was you pay too much attention to what people say. It's how people act that's important."

"Does that mean that someday you'll marry me?" I asked, teasing him this time.

In the dark, he sounded beat. "I love you. I like the way it is now. I don't want to change anything and getting married will change the whole game. If I have a wife, my kids won't be here helping me. The boys won't be here to play cards and watch the games. Virginia won't keep my house and cook for me. Dorothy won't come to stay on vacation. Because I would have a wife, they wouldn't take responsibility for me. But you don't want to be that kind of a wife."

And for the first time in eighteen years, I heard what he was saying. I didn't say anything because there wasn't anything to say. Because most of the time, I was pretty happy myself. God knows I wasn't good at being married. It wasn't one of my strengths. But I did want Mario to *want* to marry me! I hated not having a choice.

I was almost asleep when I heard Mario say, "You do know, if you really wanted to be married, we'd be married, don't you?"

"No, I don't know that," I said. "It just feels like fancy footwork when you make believe you're giving me a choice."

"I am giving you a choice," he said, "I asked if you wanted my name and you said no. I asked if you wanted to move in with me and you said no. He reached over and took my hand. "Over all these years you've only said yes to one thing."

"What?" I said. "It would be nice to hear something I said yes to."

"I asked if you wanted to be a writer, no matter what. You said 'yes.' Without any conditions, without any questions, without the need to understand. Go with your strength. Go be a writer, and stop trying to take the easy way out!"

I reached over and swatted him. "You're a lunatic," I said. "A true crazy person."

"But you are worthy of me, my dear," Mario concluded with a smile.

Chapter 41

It was several weeks later after I had been working furiously on several of my books, "Then An Angel Came" about the death of my grandson, and "The Azurite"—a book about an extra terrestrial scientist who had come to earth to help halt its destruction—when I needed to talk to Mario. I had just gotten a brilliant idea!

I drove over to his house, dying to tell him everything I had been doing. "Mario, Mario, I finally got it. I finally figured it out," I said as I ran into his study. "I finally found the answer."

Mario was sitting at his desk in his worn leather chair, hunched over one of his manuscripts, rewriting.

"Good," he said, absently. "Good Girl."

"Mario," I said, walking close to him. "I'm serious. I've been reading like a madwoman, meditating like a yogi, and I finally got it."

Now he stopped, sat up straight and picked up a huge black cigar. He unwrapped it and handed me the golden cigar band which I automatically slid on my left pointer finger. Then he slowly rolled the cigar between his lips, lifted a long wooden match out of the box, lit it, and puffed on the cigar until the smoke blew in big fluffy circles. "What did you finally get?" he asked and though his voice was even, his eyes twinkled with amusement.

I sat down on the chair opposite his. "The answer to everything," I said. 'I get how it all works now.'

"*Everything?*" he said, digesting it. Then he took a long drag of his cigar and leaned back in his chair. "Okay," he said, "I'm game."

"The Prince, the frog, Life, all of it," I said excited. "I had a moment of complete clarity when everything made complete sense."

"A trick of the mind my dear," Mario said, but then he listened. He was the best listener I ever met. It was one of the sexiest things about him.

"I know how to remove the curse. I know how to turn the frog into a Prince. I know the truth behind the fairy tale."

"Serious business," Mario said, only half teasing. "I'm a patient man."

"Okay, listen," I said, "The Princess has to see the Prince before the frog can be transformed. I mean past all the junk, past his slimy skin, past his green color, past all the croaking and jumping around. When she looks at him, she has to really see him. She can't see a frog or he can never be a prince. Through her eyes, he is only the Prince. She has to treat him like a prince, not in silly superficial ways but in real ways. She has to see his potential even before he can. Then the curse is removed and the spell is broken."

Mario tilted his head. "Makes sense," he said.

"I hear a 'but' there," I said, frowning. "What's the 'but?'"

Mario took another long drag on his cigar and now he leaned forward. "But...in this age post feminism, where are you going to find a girl like that?" he asked.

"Oh, Mario, don't kid around," I said. "She has to be a visionary. She has to be a healer. She has to be smart. Actually, she has to be *me*."

Mario laughed until tears ran down his cheeks. "You are a funny little thing," he said. "But you suit me. Now can we have dinner? I've been working like crazy all day. It's been a really good day. "

"You don't believe me," I said, disappointed.

He looked surprised. "Of course I believe you," he said. "But what has that got to do with anything?"

"It has to do with *everything*," I said. "That's how it all works. That's how life works. That's the magic. But first you have to see it! Beneath the surface of things is the truth of things."

"It's easier to recognize a princess if she's a tall blond," he said simply.

"Hey, do you think I ever imagined a short, fat little Italian, dressed in tights would come riding up on his trusty white steed to rescue me?"

"That's how you see me?" he asked.

"Of course not," I said. "I see you as I always have in all our lives together. I see you as a gorgeous Roman warrior or Egyptian Prince, golden helmet and all."

"How can such an intelligent girl believe in that nonsense?" he asked.

"How can such a smart man not?" I asked. Then I shook my head, gave up, got up, and went downstairs and started to cook us dinner.

It was another of those weekends when Mario and I were locked in his upstairs study, sitting across from each other, on opposite sides of what Mario and I called "the Pink Palermo room," writing. I was at my computer, he was at his trusty black manual typewriter. Silent. During those weekends, we did a lot of parallel play, and we talked very little.

"Want to go into town Friday night?" Mario asked suddenly spinning his office chair around toward me.

"For what?" I asked, spinning my own chair around to face him.

"Bert's finished his novel on Richard III," Mario said, "Joni Evans is giving him a party and his wife, Barbara, called today to ask if we would come."

Mario usually hates going to parties, he's basically shy and feels socially uncomfortable. But anything that involved Bert was an automatic yes.

"Sure," I said. "You feeling good enough to go?"

"I want to help Bert celebrate his book," Mario explained. "Besides, he amazes me. With everything else he has to do, he still writes all the time. I don't know how he gets all that done."

That Friday night we took a limo into New York City.

Upstairs, Joni greeted us first, with Bert and Barbara right behind. There were several pretty young women editors and their assistants—smart, independent, well dressed and respectful who immediately surrounded Mario. He looked over at me, and I smiled at him. It tickled me that people were so impressed with him, and that he was so surprised by it. He never quite got it.

After Mario briefly looked over the table filled with large square plates of hors d'oeuvres—stuffed celery, cut broccoli, cheese, rolled chicken, ham and cheese and all kinds of wines and soda, he moved over to a small chair across the room. His legs still hurt from the neuropathy and so standing was still painful.

From the time he sat down, several people came over to speak to him. Laughing, sharing stories about how they had first discovered his books, inviting him to be on a TV show or do an interview, or go to another party. Mario smiled warmly, truly interested, listened intently—just like one of the benevolent Dons in his books.

Suddenly, two really attractive young women came over and because there were no available chairs, sat on the carpet at his feet, and began to share stories of how his books had become part of their lives.

One of them was especially bright and pretty. She looked up at Mario and told him, "I loved your book, The Godfather, and those movies have become such a tradition in our family. From the time I can remember, every Christmas when our whole family gets together for the holiday, we sit around the whole day and watch all the Godfather movies. Godfather I first, before the appetizers. Godfather II comes before the macaroni and our main meal, and Godfather III before dessert. Every Christmas. We've done it so long that it's become a real tradition in our family."

As Mario looked at her, I saw a fleeting expression of confusion pass across his face. Then he reached down and gently touched the girl's cheek. I was surprised because he was usually much more reserved. The young woman looked up at Mario and smiled. "You have no idea how much pleasure those movies have brought our family," she said. "

Mario had a great smile. And now as he sat up straight, he smiled with real warmth and affection. "I thank you for the compliment," he said to the young woman. "But the Godfather? On Christmas? My dear, they were after all, criminals."

I smiled because he actually looked concerned, but it was funny.

The young woman was obviously sincere when she explained, "Still, our family always has a wonderful holiday watching that story of your family. So I just wanted you to know."

Mario shyly nodded his acknowledgement. Once she got up to mix with others in the room, Mario said to me, "What a sweet girl she is. And smart."

"You have done serious damage to the women's lib movement," I said laughing. "Good God, what a memory this life will be for you. An old Italian with young women at his feet, looking up in admiration."

"My dear," Mario said. "That young woman is evidence of the success of feminism. She's bright but she's also a true romantic. She'll be a very successful editor, and if she works hard, maybe someday she'll have her own publishing house."

He was a visionary for the truth is, that girl does now have her own publishing house.

Chapter 42

Over the next years, Mario's legs began to bother him more and more, and the best neurologist I knew, Dr. Gary Gerard, diagnosed it as a neuropathy, which is usually permanent but in Mario's case, the nerves could be repaired but it would take quite a long time. During this period, he didn't want to travel, and he preferred to stay home.

We spent so much time in his study with me sitting at my computer researching and typing and Mario lying on his couch staring at the ceiling that he began calling it, "Devils Island."

Mario had a big new study built on stilts high above the patio below so we would each have a private space to write our books. He had ceiling to floor arched windows installed so each of us could face outside and look at the trees. We sat back to back across the room from each other, each of lost in our own world for hours. Usually there was a lot of silence, but occasionally Mario would speak and then we'd take a break and listen to music or talk to each other. I loved the intimacy of that time we spent together.

Now, the kids could go home for the weekend. I'd go over on Friday nights and stay until Monday morning. It was perfect. We'd brainstorm, write, then I could cook dinner and play house for the weekend. By the time Monday morning came both of us were ready to get back to real life.

One day during the weekend, I was writing in the study we now shared.

"You going to write today Mario?" I called across the room to him one Saturday morning after we'd had breakfast.

"I *am* writing," he answered.

"I don't hear anything, and what I see is a man lying on his couch," I said. "I don't see anything that vaguely resembles writing going on."

Mario sat up on the couch, his legs crossed, feet resting on the wooden cocktail table in front of him. That table was stacked full of books, at least twenty of them. Mario read voraciously, at least one or two books a day.

He reached over and lit one of his large dark cigars. "I am writing," he repeated. "It's not coming bad."

'Okay," I said, laughing. "Let me read a few pages so I can see how it sounds."

"You've got to wait until I type them," he said.

"So you admit you haven't written anything," I said.

He shook his head and said, "You don't get it. By the time I sit down to type my first draft, my books are already written."

"What does that mean?" I asked.

"What looks like me lying on the couch resting, reading, playing cards is just me waiting for the characters to show up," he said. "When they show up, I let them tell their stories. When they finish, I type."

"You're teasing me right?" I asked.

He looked surprised. "Why would I try to put one over on you?" he asked. "You said you wanted to be a writer."

"I do," I said. "But are you being funny intentionally or is this just how you think?"

"I was answering your question," he said, and then, as though the conversation had been settled, he picked up his book again and went back to reading. "Would you get me a diet Coke?" he asked.

"Sure," I said. There was a small refrigerator in his room, stocked with diet Cokes, who his kids, like magical helpers, made sure was always full.

Mario wrote most of his first drafts by hand with a black, green or red felt magic marker on a long legal pad. Whenever he felt blocked and couldn't think of anything, he swore the pressure of the pen on his fingertips helped set the story free.

Unfortunately, he scribbled and his handwriting was completely illegible. I mean even to him.

Thank God for all my years of nursing when life and death depended on my ability to decipher a doctor's orders for treatment or medication, or I would have been lost. After studying Mario's handwriting and with a lot of practice, I was able to translate the mystery symbols of his hieroglyphics and type them into my computer. Those pages I typed from his handwritten originals saved him from the dreaded "blank" page and gave him a rough first draft of his own work. The first time I saw his rough draft, I couldn't believe it could ever wind up being a book. Despite the fact that by the time we met, he had already written "The Fortunate Pilgrim", "Dark Arena", and the famous "The Godfather" as well as "Fools Die."

Only once, at the very beginning, did I substitute a word of mine for his and only because I couldn't make out what he had scribbled.

Later that afternoon, the moment he read it, all he said was, "God, what was I thinking here? Sounds like an English professor."

He didn't reprimand me, what he did say was, "It reminds me of the time Francis (Coppola) told me about some mafia guys sautéing onions, and all I said was, mafia guys 'fry' onions, they don't sauté. That wound up as a scene in The Godfather."

As we worked together longer and learned more about each other, even if a sentence was truly bad, I would never change it without asking him what he thought he meant.

When he couldn't decipher what he'd written, he'd say, "Put anything. I'll catch it and change it a dozen times before I turn it in." That became a funny kind of game for me. Never once did I substitute one of my words for his without him catching it on the rewrite.

"Writing is rewriting," Mario told me. "I think I've said that before."

"How many times?" I'd ask.

"As many times as it takes for you to really know your characters, for you to feel some affection for them," he told me. "And for them to be complex enough to be interesting."

When Mario was on a roll he typed on an old black metal Underwood or Royal typewriter. He was superstitious about that typewriter. Once it helped him write a bestseller. He was afraid that without it, he wouldn't be able to write another.

"The typewriter doesn't write, you do," I said laughing. "You should try writing on a computer. It will make editing so much easier. You'll be able to write your books in half the time."

"Writing is a process," he said. "You can't speed it up without losing something, its like evolution."

"Can't you just try it and see?" I asked.

It was a very long time before he finally agreed, and that was only because it got harder and harder to find ribbons for his typewriter. Besides, the metal keys were becoming so clogged with ink that I had to scrub them with a toothbrush in order for an 'o' to look like anything but a blob of ink.

One afternoon we were sitting in the study again and I could hear the click of his typewriter, harder than usual, when he finally called me over to his desk. "Can you fix this?" he asked.

I stood over his shoulder and looked at the page he just typed. It was hardly visible. "It looks as though you wrote it with invisible ink," I said. "You sure you don't want to try my computer. It would be awful to lose all your pages just because they stopped making ribbons for that typewriter."

"I'll think about it," he agreed.

"Don't take too long," I said. "Time's a wastin' and your pages are fading fast."

He called his son Gene and explained the problem but when he got off the phone, he said, "Okay, let's give it a try."

"Want to practice on my computer first?" I asked.

"No, I want to write my own stories," he said. "Our writing is different. I want my own."

"Now?" I asked.

"Sure," he said.

So I called and ordered a whole Apple computer setup. I mean a really good, top of the line, MacIntosh computer complete with a large enough screen and a printer. "It will be here tomorrow morning, before ten," I told him. "Then we can spend the rest of the weekend with me teaching you how to use it. By the time I leave on Monday morning, you'll be a pro."

"We'll give it a shot," he said.

But the expression on Mario's face when that computer arrived and I began to set it up, was all too obvious. "That screen looks like it's staring at me," he said. "It's nerve wracking. Can you move it farther away from the bedroom door?"

"Mario, it's on your desk. How much farther away can I move it and still have you be able to sit at your desk and write?"

"While you're teaching me how to use it, put it on the table over there," he said. "That way when one of the kids brings me a new ribbon, I can still use my typewriter and write the old fashioned way."

"Okay," I said. "I'll move it."

So I lugged the whole setup, TV monitor, computer console, all the cables and the printer and put it on the table in the middle of the room. "Want to try it?" I asked once I had gotten it booted up.

Mario gingerly sat on the chair and placed his fingers on the keyboard. "Why is that little light blinking at me?" he asked.

"It's just a cursor, forget it," I said. "Pay no attention. It's just there to show where your letters will begin."

"It's distracting," he said.

"Don't look at the screen then," I said. "Concentrate on what you're thinking and look at the keyboard, the way you always do on your typewriter."

He tried. He did try. But after his manual typewriter, his touch was heavy and as he banged on the keys, they repeated each letter ten times. When he finally looked up, he just shook his head.

"You don't have to hammer these keys," I explained. "You just have to touch them."

"I can't change everything about how I write my books," he said. "Look at all the spelling mistakes. It will take twice as long at this rate."

"No," I said. "Watch this." I launched the spelling checker and one by one it corrected the spelling until we had a perfect copy. But when I looked at Mario's expression, I knew we were in big trouble.

"What's wrong?" I asked. "Isn't this amazing? See what I mean about making the editing easier?"

Mario pushed back his chair and moved away from the table. "Get that out of here," he said.

I frowned. "What are you talking about?"

"Get that whole thing out of here," he repeated. "Every piece of it. I don't want even a memory of it in my study or it will ruin this book."

I couldn't help myself, I began to laugh again. "Mario, what are you saying? What just happened?"

"Take it out of here," he repeated.

I asked, "What do you want me to do with it?"

"I don't care," he said. "Put it in your car, take it to your house, just get it out of my study before it does serious damage."

Because Mario looked so nervous, I carried the whole setup downstairs and put it in my trunk. It was so big that I had to put the monitor on the back seat.

When I came back upstairs, he was sitting on the couch reading. "Thank you," he said. "That's much better. Eugene got me some ribbons and he's bringing them over."

I sat down on the couch next to him. "What happened?" I asked again. "What went wrong?'

Mario closed his book and put it down on the cocktail table in front of us.

"Carol," he said seriously, "Did you see the way that machine changed my words?"

"Mario," I said, "It didn't change the words, it corrected the spelling."

"It changed some of my sentences," he insisted. "If it can do that, it can change my story. It's my story, and I don't want anyone or anything to change that."

"Mario," I said, "It's a machine. It can only do what you tell it to do. Once you learn it's language, it will make life much easier."

"Not for me," he said. "If it can do that, it can do other things. If it knows how to spell, it can learn how to plot, and I can't write with something in my room trying to out plot me."

I just shook my head.

Then he added, "Plus, I certainly couldn't sleep in my room, knowing that it was in here ...plotting. I couldn't shut my eyes."

"You're not serious, are you?" I asked him.

"Serious enough. I don't ever want to see that thing again," he said.

"But Mario," I said, "That doesn't make sense. You've been living with my computers for years. They never bothered you. You never even noticed them."

Mario frowned. "Why would I care if your computer changed your stories? Why would I care if your computer plotted against you?"

"Okay, I give up," I said. "You've got a science fiction mind. It's a damn machine."

"Honey," Mario said, "Don't be mad. It's a good thing that we found out I hate computers. That I don't like it fixing my spelling and changing my grammar."

"Why would that be?" I asked. "Why would you not want something that made your writing easier?"

Then Mario smiled. "Because if that computer could do what you say, I'd have to get rid of you," he said.

Chapter 43

The Christmas that Mario surprised me the most, I was completely unprepared.

Each year for every holiday, he would ask me what I wanted as a gift, and each year I would tell him, "A computer or a printer, or a scanner or a hard drive. Or a stove with a glass top because you know how much I love to cook. Or even a new set of pots. Something that helps me be more productive. Those are the kind of gifts I like."

For the first few years he didn't mind. He always bought me some piece of jewelry and sent me and my Family an indecently huge floral arrangement for a holiday centerpiece. Plus, he always bought us our Holiday dinner. I mean, because each of us ate with our own families for the holidays, Virginia and I would go shopping and buy all the food for both families: two huge Prime Ribs or two 26 lb turkeys and all the trimmings. Each of our families filled a long table and it would take hours and days of cooking beforehand.

For my family's holidays, my mother, my sister Bibs, my daughter Teri, my niece, Jenny plus all our closest friends and all the grandchildren would cook and serve. After dinner, my son Danny and the boys would do the dishes and help clean up.

At Mario's, Virginia was in charge and all the daughters-in-law chipped in. We often teased that we'd have to rent a hall if we were to combine our family dinners for the holidays, and so we just never did.

Afterwards, either I would go over to Mario's to say hi to every-one, or he would come to my house, so that usually each of us saw both families for the holidays.

Virginia and I spent weeks before every holiday shopping for both our families, and the huge packages we had to pull and drag, took several all-day trips to the malls and Christmas stores. Those shopping trips were both the happiest times and some of the tough-est times I've ever had.

On the days I didn't shop with Virginia, my daughter, Teri, or my sister Bibs and I shopped for all the kids and really close friends. Thousands of decisions, hundreds of presents, and all the wrapping that followed.

But for us, it wasn't a material thing. I wanted everyone to have at least one very special day that was magical for them. That made them each feel special. It wasn't the gift that I bought that counted, it was that they knew they'd been heard. So all year long I listened to what each person needed, wanted, and wished for and then if possible, I would try to get it for them. It was a huge amount of work—making all those dreams come true. Still, that was the love in Christmas.

There were so many years that I was too poor to buy anyone anything, that playing Santa Claus, or the Giving Angel, brought me more joy than any gift I received. Mario didn't understand all the "presents" stuff, but still because Virginia and I thought it was important, he always supported our plan and gave us each the same amount of money to spend! Too much.

Two nights before Christmas, I was over his house cooking din-ncr, while he was sitting at the table reading, when I said, "Ma-rio, please don't waste your money on flowers and jewelry again. I don't like to own anything or wear anything that is too much responsibility so I put it away and then I hardly ever see it again. I don't want to have to worry about losing anything that costs too much."

"Okay," he said, but he hardly looked up, still his voice sounded funny.

"What?" I asked. "I hurt your feelings?"

"No, no," he said. "It's just that you make me *scumbadi* (his word for losing face) if after all this time..." His voice faded away.

"Okay," I said. "Buy me anything. Make it big, make it gaudy, show me who you really are!!" Then I laughed. "I will sacrifice again to make you look good to your family and friends."

"You're such a good girl," he said looking up and smiling. "Such a good mafia girl."

On Christmas Eve, when Mario came over to my house, everyone was already there. There were so many brightly wrapped Christmas packages, they filled half the living room. Every other square inch was filled with people spilling from the kitchen and the dining room. Several small groups were sitting around my study, and even on the couches in my sitting room. The tree was lit up, Christmas songs were playing in the background and the sounds of laughter and kids and the smell of my sister's meatballs, frying, wafted into the living room making everything seem as warm and comforting as those Christmas Cards I always bought and never got around to sending.

It all started around nine, when the kids got to open their presents first. Good planning because then they could play and stay out of our way so that after Midnight Mass, the grownups could open their presents in peace. It always worked, but of course, not perfectly.

My father would always look around and say, "What a sin..." thinking of all those who had neither food nor family.

I walked past, kissed him in greeting, and said "Stop! If we had less, they wouldn't have more. Enjoy us."

Mario and my father sat on the couch next to each other, with the same expression on their faces—pleased that they had been fortunate enough to provide for their families.

It was a noisy happy Christmas dance that our family was doing, and the following day, Mario's would do the same.

My favorite time of every Christmas Eve was after everyone had gone home, and Mario and I could sit together, listening to soft Christmas music in the quiet darkness with only the colorful lights from the Christmas tree blinking. It was then we would thank each other for the year we'd shared, and wish each other more. More happiness, more wishes come true, more health and good fortune. It was the real Christmas for me. With no one else around but us, I could feel it. All the love and gratitude for our lives and our families.

It was then, sitting in the almost dark, that Mario pulled a small box out of his pocket and handed it to me.

"What is this?" I asked.. "You already gave me a stove, a scanner and a new laptop."

"Just a little something extra," he said and smiled. "Open it."

Sometime a heart is filled to bursting. Sometimes there are no wishes left to come true. Sometimes life offers more than you ask for, and sometimes that's almost too much. I opened the box. "A diamond ring?" I asked, surprised, "a beautiful diamond ring."

"Is that what you see?" he asked, and then he handed me the receipt.

"What's this?" I said. "you're not supposed to give a girl the receipt with the present."

He smiled again. "Read it," he said.

"Engagement ring," was underlined. I shook my head and turned to him.

"Stop hollering you don't know our relationship. Now, you have a title."

"What title?" I asked, puzzled.

"*My fianceé,*" he said, twinkling. "Feel better now that I *own* you? Now that your *mine*?"

I laughed and kissed him. "You're renting. Not buying," I said. But I was touched. Truly.

Mario shook his head, smiling and said, "*My wild horse.* Now, that truly is funny."

Chapter 44

The following month, Mario and I took a quick trip to Atlantic City to gamble for the weekend. But it was truly awful. It looked just like a fake Vegas. Not even a good copy. The food was not nearly as good, the hotels were just kind of crummy and we were not having a good time. The final straw was that in the middle of the night, the fire alarms went off and Mario and I were standing outside in the cold, shivering. My nightmare. It was so bad, I started to laugh.

Mario asked me, "If we had to flee the house because it was on fire, and you could only grab one thing, what one thing would you take as you ran?"

I laughed. "You mean what would I grab besides you?"

He didn't say anything but his eyes twinkled.

I'm serious," he said, "I'm curious."

"Only one thing?" I asked.

He nodded and waited while I thought about it for a few minutes.

"You won't believe this," I said. "It's so cliché that it will probably surprise you as much as it surprises me." I held up my hand in front of me so both of us could see. "My diamond ring, the one you gave me."

Mario frowned but his eyes glimmered. "You're a hopeless romantic," he said. "I thought you were serious about being a writer."

"What does that mean?"

"A real writer would grab manuscript pages."

"Wrong," I said. "A man writer would grab manuscript pages. A real woman who was a writer would take the ring, knowing she has another copy of her manuscript somewhere else. Besides, women can multitask. If I had to, I'd grab the ring and the manuscript pages."

"Men are simpler creatures," he said. "They do one thing at a time."

I laughed at him. "You are a maniac. Besides, I can always rewrite the pages to any story I'm working on. I can always tell the story over again. I can do a rewrite. But diamonds are forever. This ring is the proof that you really do love me, and even better, its proof that we didn't make each other up. With so little magic left in the world today, it's the one magical symbol that proves we did live, find true love, even in this cynical world at this time. Besides, it appeals not to the warrior woman in me, but to that woman in me who still believes in fairy tales with Happily Ever After endings."

One night several months later, Mario and I were in the study when he said, "You know I appreciate all the help you give me, right?"

"Yep," I said, "I do."

He got off the couch and walked over to his desk. He sat in his big leather chair, and as I always did, I pulled up a chair across from him, alongside his desk.

"I don't mean only helping me when I'm sick," he said. "I mean the help with the writing. All the editing and typing. And all the rest."

I laughed. "That's the easy part," I said. "It's built in my genes."

He nodded, but looked serious. "I have something I want to show you," he said. He reached into the bottom draw of his desk and pulled out a bunch of papers.

"What's that?" I asked.

He handed it to me. I'm sure I looked surprised. It was a screenplay of my book The Nurse's Story. He had called it GWYN. (Go Wherever You're Needed)

"Mario," I said. "I thought you had agreed that your readers wanted gangster books from you?"

"This I did to please myself, and for you," he said simply.

I was touched but I didn't know what to say.

"Read it," he said. "It won't take long. Screenplays are only about 120 pages."

So, I read it.

"Mario," I said. "I love you. I do. I so appreciate that you took all this time away from your own work to do this. But even I'm confused. It's like Coke making jeans. It's not your brand, not your style."

He frowned. "You don't see it" he asked. "You can't see what I've done?"

I hesitated. "Mario I am so sorry, and I know all the stereotypes are reflections of the thinking of a culture. But here you still have nurses being party girls and you still have them falling in love with doctors or patients."

"Honey," he said and this time he was sterner than usual. "You have to take a reader from something he or she knows before you can take them farther. Unless you're writing science fiction, you've got to give them some ground to stand on. Then you move them a little farther. Evolution takes time."

I nodded.

"Okay," I said. "I get some of that. But what is it that you see?"

He took a deep breath. "What I see is 'The Three Musketeers and D'Artangnon.' I see in your book, what I know to be true. A real woman's adventure story. I mean women playing to their own strengths not following a male myth."

"Women's strengths?" I asked.

"Their ability to care for and protect the people they care about. Taking care of sick people. Like they do with children or older people. There, women have such an edge over most men. They can do anything. They're tougher, they can endure the most awful tragedies in life and still make tough decisions."

"Okay," I said. "I can see that...and I thank you for being able to see it. But what are you planning to do with it?"

"With your permission, I'm going to send it to Bert with a letter telling him how much I believe in it." Then Mario looked at me and said, "I want you to tell me anything that you see wrong with it in a technical medical sense. But I want only my name on it."

"Okay," I said. "I don't mind that at all."

"I want you to know I wrote it for you," he said. "I only want my name on it because Hollywood will pay more that way. Besides, you still hold all the cards because it's your book they have to buy first—this is an adaptation. So that means you always have veto power."

I got up bent down and kissed him on the forehead. "I do love you too," I said. "Let's see what Bert has to say."

I do believe that Bert agreed with me, that Mario's audience wanted gangsters from Mario, but Spelling Productions made us an offer anyway.

Mario was happy with it. "We get less up front, but a big bonus on the back end."

He showed me the contracts. I read them and shook my head.

"You said I have veto power," I said softly. "I can't do this Mario. Not only because of all the reasons I gave you. But for a much bigger reason. Spelling wants to buy my characters, just like Paramount bought yours, so you could never use the Corleone's again. Paramount owns them and any other stories you wanted to use those characters in, has to have permission from Paramount and a cut for Paramount. It feels wrong to me, Mario. I am so sorry."

Mario didn't try to talk me out of it. He was just quiet for a long time. When he spoke he sounded as though he understood. "It's okay, kid," he said smiling. "I really hoped you would like it. That you would see how strong those nurses, those women are, in that screenplay, and in the world. But take it anyway. I mean, I do get a million dollars a screenplay. Someday it may be worth something to you."

He handed it to me, and I took it. I so wished I could have thanked him in a much bigger way, but even then, though he didn't know it, it was worth far more than a million dollars to me just because he had done it.

Several months passed and Mario continued to work, but still struggled some to get the work the way he wanted it. He got tired more easily, and his legs bothered him more often but still he always knew what he wanted to do and kept rewriting until he got it right.

Often, now, he would show me his pieces and I would just ask questions for him to clarify what he wanted. No one else could read his writing, and he was scribbling even more. I used to laugh that he was an impressionistic writer.

We had been researching the Borgias and Medici again. He always went back to that period and those characters when he needed the comfort of hanging out with them. When other ideas or characters hadn't shown up yet. And so between the work on my own books, I often sat and read to Mario or discussed some of the dynamics of the Popes, which amused him.

We were getting close to the final draft of The Last Don when one night over dinner, he asked me, "Do you know how many women have sabotaged their own careers whenever they fell in love with a man?"

"Nope," I said. "Not one of my concerns. Couldn't do it."

"I'm serious," he said. "They meet a guy and suddenly he becomes their manager, and disaster usually follows."

"Your point, sir?" I asked.

I was cleaning off the table, putting the dishes in the sink, and he was helping me, when he asked, "Can we go upstairs? I have something to ask you."

"Sure," I said. "No problem."

Upstairs, instead of sitting on the couch, he sat at his desk again. And again, I sat opposite.

"What's the deal, boss?" I asked teasing him.

"Since I've been sick, I've been losing some of my confidence," he said. "I've begun to worry more."

"About dying?" I asked.

"No," he said. "About the work. I can't focus as well and I have so many people on my payroll, that I'm afraid I'm not going to be able to get it all done. Then everyone will be in trouble. I will not have done my duty to them."

"How can I help?" I asked.

"You know how I always say I don't collaborate till after I'm dead?" he asked. "You know how I don't want anyone else to interfere with how I write my books?"

"Yes," I said. "Well," he said, "I've been giving it a lot of thought. Over these years you've become a great editor. You know my work even better than I do. You know how I always tell you how smart you are, how much talent you have?"

"Mario, please say what you need to? The suspense is killing me."

He got up and began to pace. "This is a big thing I'm going to ask. And I'm going to tell you, if you asked me, I couldn't do it. I couldn't say yes."

"Okay," I said. "That's a hook...Now tell me what you want?"

"I figure that if The Last Don does alright, I only need to write two more books to give everyone some time. If they've saved a little, they'll be okay. But, I write slow and it takes me a long time to get out a book."

"You're not going to ask me to write your books are you? Cause I cannot do that," I said. "Some of that gangster stuff drives me crazy. And the women...oh my God, Mario. Look at the fights we've already had over that."

For the first time, Mario laughed. "No, but you're getting warm. Could you make my books our priority for the next couple of books? Just to give everyone a shot?"

"What does that mean?" I asked.

"I mean if you see a place where I repeat, or if I get off track, will you put your work aside for a bit to help me out?"

"So you're talking editing?" I asked. "Only quicker editing?"

"More or less," he said. "But nagging, brainstorming, finding the flaws in my logic.."

"Don't I already do that?" I asked. "I mean even on The Last Don, didn't I disagree and you still did what you wanted?"

"Sure," he said. "But I'm asking if we get into a pinch, can you put your own work aside to help with mine? You write faster than I do, and you have more time cause you can put it through your computer..."

"You ask me this after you've already told me how many women sabotage their careers for the men they love?" I said. "You are funny."

"Just think about it honey," he said. "Don't answer right away. I know what I'm asking."

"You want to manage me?" I asked, laughing.

He frowned. "No," he said. "Never. Bad odds."

"Then it's a yes," I said. "It's a yes for such a simple reason. Because I could never sacrifice the many for the one—because they are all family. Mine or yours."

He hugged me then. "Thank you," he said.

"Thank you," I said.

Chapter 45

We were finally almost finished with The Last Don and the publishers wanted Mario to do a publicity tour: TV, radio and print.

"A book should be able to stand on it's own merit," he insisted. "Anything I say or do could ruin its chances."

"That's not what you said when you told me to tour with my books," I said. "I had to do 21 cities with 'The Nurse's Story' and about the same with 'Rusty's Story.'" I didn't like it, but it did help sell books!

But Mario hated to do promotion for any book. He actually was a very private person and didn't like publicity of any kind. He was shy and could gather his thoughts more easily on paper where he could later edit and be clearer about what he meant.

"You're better talking off the cuff than I am," he said. "Plus the camera likes you better than it likes me. You gave your book the chance it needed. Besides, you had a mission, I have a book."

Now, Mario had *the look*. The look that meant the discussion was over. But his publishers really thought they needed him to hit the media circuits. They felt it had been too long since he had written 'The Godfather' and they wanted people to remember he was it's creator. 'Fool's Die' and 'The Fourth K' were better books in Mario's opinion but they insisted that his audience wanted gangster books from him. So even though Mario wanted to give his readers something new and different to think about, he finally relented and admitted that if he wanted to please them, he should write what the audience wanted.

"Like I said before, I have no right to expect them to indulge me in my eccentricity."

"Godfather Papers, right?" I asked him. I had read that book and loved it, especially because he has so many personal stories in it. More than anything else, the journal at the end, absolutely blew me away.

Still, I knew not to push too hard when Mario stood his ground. It would only force him to stand stronger, so for hours I just went back to work, typing, rewriting and reading.

Finally, that night, as we lay in bed in the dark, I asked, "Hey Mario, if I'm right and you do get to come back to earth again next life, what would you want to be?"

He didn't hesitate a minute. "A baseball player," he said.

"Cool," I said. "But baseball stars have to do a lot of media..."

Destiny sometimes steps in when it's needed. That night Mario had a dream. A dream so vivid and so real that he actually fell out of bed! Thump, was all I heard. When I leaned over the side of the bed, there he was, still asleep, with a smile on his face.

"Mario?" I called, reaching down to touch him. "Are you okay?"

He opened his eyes and looked around, puzzled.

"What's going on?" I asked him.

He got up and sat on the bed. "Don't know," he said. "Last thing I know I was running across the field trying to catch a fly ball!! It was amazing!"

"Did you catch it?" I asked.

"You woke me up!" he said.

"Well, if I were you, I'd try to get a jump on those media tours," I said. "I mean you could use the practice."

I didn't find out until the following week, that Mario agreed to do a tour. Charlie Rose, Larry King Live, and other big shows. When I asked him about it he said, "I'll do it, but you'll do it with me, right?"

"Is that an ask?" I teased him.

"Honey," he said. "It's your duty to support me. You know this stuff, I don't. Besides, it will be a strain on my health."

"You're funny," I said. "Lanetta can go with you too on some of the West coast stuff, right. So we're good. Glad you're looking forward...a baseball player, hmmm.."

One of the biggest surprises I had was how much Mario enjoyed book signings at the book stores. The one that was most special was at Barnes and Noble. As the limo drove up to the bookstore, Mario pointed out the window at the long lines of people and asked, "Hey what's going on?"

It was Lanetta who told him, "It's for you, Boss, all those people are waiting to meet you for you to sign their books."

Mario was shocked. Once inside the big bookstore, they had a table all set up for Mario with big lights and cameras. There was a very large stack of books and pens. Mario sat at the table and I stood behind him as I watched one after another person come up to meet and talk to him.

Several times the store manager or the publicity director tried to speed the people up and encouraged Mario to write less or speak less, but he wouldn't. He asked almost everyone about their lives and was truly interested. He had been signing for almost two hours, when he called me over to the table. "Honey," he said, "There are still so many people, there are even women holding their babies."

"I know," I said. "And still a long line outside..."

He looked stricken. "Honey, it's almost dinner time. I can't go faster."

"It's okay," I said. "Everyone seems pleased. They love that you're talking to them."

The next time he called me over, it was starting to get dark. "Honey," he said. "We still have an hour or more to go. It's getting late. I heard a baby crying. Could you asked Lanetta or one of the publicity guys to order pizza for everyone. Tell them I said it's on the house."

So I did. Boxes and Boxes of pizza were carried in and passed around until everyone was happy, no one went hungry, and all the books had been signed.

Mario was a happy man.

The Final Chapter

Chapter 46

It was in May, that much I remember, when I suddenly understood that my life would change forever, that it would never again be the same. Grace stepped in and covered my eyes, put cotton in my ears, silenced my mind, so I couldn't hear the shattering sound of the breaking of my heart. God's mercy when life plays so rough that you can no longer bear it.

It was a whisper, not a scream. Not even a shout. I was lying in bed next to Mario watching him sleep and I just knew. I got that pain in my stomach, the warning. The space in the bed next to me, his side of the bed, was suddenly empty. I blinked, sat up, and he was back. But, in that one moment, I understood. I knew it would be soon. Mario was going to die.

I'd spent so much time focusing on him, juggling between being his nurse, his lover, his best buddy, his protector, that I hadn't considered what it would mean to me not to have him around any longer.

I tried to take a deep breath in, to relax, but it was so sharp, it cut. I felt halved. No longer me without him. I didn't know I felt like that. I didn't know with all our fancy footwork, with all our shadow boxing, he'd still manage to knock me out. I couldn't stay another minute. I couldn't run. There was no turning back now. I understood.

I tried to steel myself, I tried to brace myself for the next hard blow, but when he woke in the morning, he smiled and just said, "Hi honey," like every other morning.

For once I couldn't share. I couldn't talk to him, I couldn't name my fear, I couldn't help him prepare. I couldn't ask him to help prepare me.

I ran home that morning, and climbed into my own bed. I told everyone I had a cold. Something. The following morning, I called the doctor. He ordered an antibiotic. I took it, and within minutes passed out cold.

The next thing I remember was that my son Danny and my favorite girls, Lynn and Rhonda, were in the living room, and I could hear the radio sounds of a police car. The ambulance came. I remember being lifted onto the gurney and marveling at how beautiful the sky was. There was still a sky, I was surprised. Two EMT guys lifted me into the ambulance and drove away.

By the time I got to the hospital I was hemorrhaging. From everywhere. I bled for days. The doctors couldn't stop it. They didn't know what caused it. But I knew. By June 2, the bleeding stopped. It was over. I had been in the hospital for over a week.

I talked to Mario every day. He was very concerned, he wanted to come to see me, but I begged him not to. I told him I didn't want to have to worry about him too. I knew he'd be upset. His kids came. His and Erika's. My kids and my family came and stayed.

When I was released from the hospital, there was no diagnosis except possible antibiotic reaction. But I knew. I'd heard the ripping of my soul.

The next month was the hardest of my life. The kids had gotten Mario a nurse to help care for him. I was angry. Furious that I had so quickly been replaced. Even my books and toiletries had been taken away from my side of the bed, and put in drawers.

Roseanne, was her name, the nurse, and she was young and pretty. A 'Victoria's Secret' Nurse. I met her in the hospital when I went to see Mario, because he also had an episode the day before my release: his pacemaker failed. I watched his nurse carefully.

She was good. She had energy, she was young, and on that day I felt 100 years old. More than that, she was cheerful. I could see she loved nursing and she loved taking care of Mario. I should have been relieved, but I wasn't.

Mario, sitting up in bed, in that hospital, explained, "I don't want you to be my nurse. As I get sicker, I don't want you to have to take care of me. I just want you to talk to me and make me laugh."

"Of course," I said. "But I don't mind taking care of you." Yet, I knew I wasn't strong enough yet, and as I looked at Roseanne teasing him, and flirting with him, and loving what she was doing, I knew I could never offer him what she could now. She offered him distraction, caring, and hope. She truly believed she could "save" him, and I knew in my heart and soul, that I could not give him that. Not anymore.

Roseanne came home with him to take care of him, to make him get up, to encourage him to eat, to make sure he did his exercise. To make sure he put as much effort as he could into getting well. I saw in her what I saw in myself when I was younger, and I was mourning that as well.

She smiled with joy when she spoke to him. She danced into his study to bring him his meds, and even as he got sicker, and sicker, she stayed constant. Trying and often succeeding where I couldn't even pretend. The kids did everything for him that Roseanne couldn't, and I stayed over to keep him company. We talked about writing, we talked about life, we talked about all my books and his.

I can't remember when he started to lose his hearing, but he did start going deaf from the antibiotics he took and so even our jokes didn't work as well. Our timing was off.

I tried to be supportive, but I didn't like his doctor at all. I thought he was over conscientious, too ambitious, and did too many tests and treatments that couldn't change the outcome. But Mario liked him. Had confidence in him. I had to move out of the way.

There were only two scenes that I remember in every detail, two scenes that etched themselves in every cell that I am...

Mario had gotten so sick that his heart was failing, nothing to be done anymore because his heart muscle was too weak. He couldn't walk now, except to the bathroom, and he wore Oxygen most of the time. His favorite nephew, his lawyer, Arthur, spent time with him. Lanetta had flown up to see him, many of his friends stopped by to visit and the kids were always around. One slept over every night in case we needed them.

That night the nurse and I walked him over to the couch in his study so he could sit up. I sat alongside him for a while and then kneeled on the rug in front of him. "You look rather dashing dressed in oxygen," I told him.

He smiled weakly at me. "You are such a funny little thing," he said.

"I hope you appreciate that," I said.

He tilted his head then and asked, "Do you love me?"

"I do," I said.

"Why?" he asked.

I shook my head. "I don't know. You're funny, generous, smart... but none of that really matters. I guess if I could say why I loved you, then once those things were gone, I wouldn't love you any more."

"Be honest with me," he said. "Tell me the truth..." and I knew he really wanted to know. "Tell me some of the things that you really see in me, that you know about me."

"Okay," I said. "You are a very selfish man, as well as very generous. You are awfully tricky sometimes, but you are clueless about so many things. Yet, you're one of smartest men I've ever known. And the kindest. But given a choice, you would choose you over me and everyone else."

He nodded. "Still you love me?"

"I do," I said.

He smiled.

"Don't you think it's sad that we never had any firsts?" I asked. "I wasn't your first love, your greatest passion, the best sex partner, the most devoted wife."

He laughed. "To paraphrase someone wiser, when a man has lived a long life, and understands what is truly valuable, what is precious and important in life, it is only then that he can choose a last love."

He reached over and touched my cheek. "I chose you, my dear, to be my last love. And that is no small thing." I wanted to cry, I wanted to be mad at God, and Fate and everyone and everything else. How would I live in the world without him? How could I live at all? But I couldn't cry, not now. So I just sat on the couch next to him, and put my head on his chest. "I'm not listening to your heart beat," I said. "I love you."

He patted my head and said, "I know. I don't know why, but it's a comfort."

"Mario?" I asked him then, "What is the most valuable thing you've learned in your life?"

He patted my head again. "Never to harm another," he said quietly.

"Can I ask one more favor, please?" But I didn't wait for permission. "Give me some advice to help me live in a world without you? Tell me how?

He nodded and I could see he was getting tired, but he smiled. "Okay," he said, struggling to breathe. "Just remember this. Men are simple creatures. Don't expect of them what you do of women."

I covered my eyes with my hands, and began to cry. "I can't believe that Mario," I said. "I just can't."

He closed his eyes and smiled. "Don't say I didn't warn you," he said.

On the night that Mario died, his color was bad and he was falling in and out of consciousness. A new nurse, Mary, was with him because Roseanne had worked too many days in a row. Mary asked me to go inside and sleep on the couch so I could get some rest. She promised she would come and get me if anything changed. Tony was sleeping over that night, and so after we talked a little, Tony went into his room, I went into the study to sleep on the couch, and Mary stayed with Mario. I had been up for so many hours, that I actually fell asleep to the sound of Mario's breathing and the sound of oxygen bubbling from the next room.

I had been sleeping for just a little while when the nurse came into the study and said, "He's calling for you."

I went into the bedroom, where he was lying in bed, oxygen on, his eyes open. He patted the bed next to him. "Come to bed," he said, and to the nurse, "Get some medicine and then rest inside."

Mary walked into the study to sit on the couch, and Mario leaned over. "Come closer," he said. "Get under the covers. Lay with me." So I did, but within minutes, he asked, "Take your clothes off please. I'm getting so cold. I can't get warm."

"Mario," I said. "The nurse is inside. Tony is in the other bedroom."

"Honey," he said. "I'm cold. I'm so cold." I hesitated, but then he reached up to touch my cheek. "I promise, this is the last time I'll ask."

Afterword

2001

I was looking down at the empty bandstand on the street below, through the small window of the kitchen on the set of the "Today" show, waiting to be interviewed by Ann Curry, when I saw him being led out onto the concert stage.

A huge crowd surrounded the stage, jumping up and down, screaming and clapping. Suddenly, I had one of those ahha! moments and I knew that my whole life had been filled with miracles....but of course, not only—some of it was damn hard.

That was the moment I really understood why I had inhabited the land of myth and fairies, met real heroes and had to fight genuine dragons, who didn't even know I was driven by my mission and protected by my prayers.

In order to explain, I have to play with time, because on the day I was booked to appear on the Today show, Mario had already died, and I had promised that I would finish his book, "The Family." I had kept that promise and finished the book. That's why Ann Curry was interviewing me .

So I was here, in New York, behind the scenes at seven thirty in the morning, barely awake, waiting to be interviewed. Publicity for any book was part of the deal or it would never sell. Without TV few people would even know it was published.

The miracle was that on that day, I really understood that all of Life was planned well in advance and that even after death, you can still keep promises you make to those you've loved.

How did I know that? Mario.

I had asked Mario, if there was life after death, if he would come back and let me know. "Nope," he said. "It will ruin the surprise. You have to find out for yourself."

In the two years since Mario had died, he had never shown up.

On this day, the day of the interview, I wasn't expecting anything different.

The singing group "Destiny's Child" had been scheduled to appear on the Today show the day that I was to be interviewed and my daughter Teri and I both laughed about that, thinking it a sign.

I heard the producer say, "Destiny's Child has been cancelled...."

When she came into the Green Room, where I was waiting earlier, I had asked, "Why?"

"Don't know," she said. "We've got Andrea Bocelli. He's doing our concert today."

All I could do was laugh. Andrea Bocelli. In Concert. In a place I couldn't miss him.

I remembered that evening all those years before, when Mario and I were sitting on the couch in his study, watching and listening to a Bocelli concert on TV. We were taking a break from our writing, and I was nestled comfortably on the couch next to Mario.

He patted my head then and said with amusement in his voice, "I used to think that when you leaned your head on my chest, you were being romantic, but now I know you're just listening to my heart beat."

"Why is it not romantic to make sure your heart keeps beating regularly? If I no longer liked you, I wouldn't care what your heart was doing. So this is really romantic."

"Hmm..." was all Mario said.

"I'd like to see Bocelli in concert," I said. "How about taking me?"

"I don't go to concerts," he said. "I can't hear that well. Why don't you go with your girlfriends?"

I sat up straight and looked at him frowning. "Hey, how often do I ask you to take me anywhere? Mostly we go where you want to go. We never go anywhere that has no gambling. I want to go to a Bocelli concert with you. That's what I think is romantic."

Mario's eyes got that distant look of musings when he said, "I didn't know you liked concerts. I really didn't know you liked concerts."

"I don't," I said. "But I do really like Bocelli. He inspires me and gives me courage. I figure if he, as a blind man, is brave enough to walk out on stage and not worry about falling into the orchestra pit because his purpose is to sing, then maybe I can do anything I have to, to accomplish what I'm meant to do in life. That's why I think it would be spectacular to see and hear him up close. "

Mario looked at me, studying me. "You're a funny girl. You really minded all our trips, gambling in Las Vegas, and traveling to the Riviera, staying at the Dorchester in London, going to the film festival Cannes and gambling in Monte Carlo? I thought you enjoyed staying in Malibu on the beach during the cold winters here, and I did take you to Venice. You did like Venice, right?"

I smiled at him. "Yes, I said, "I loved Venice. And all those other places were fine too. But I didn't feel essential there, and I guess it was important for me to feel necessary."

"You were Important to me," he said. "You saved my life, which I think of as essential."

I laughed. "Okay, that wasn't bad. I felt okay when I was trying to save your life, that did give me a purpose. But it was the rest that gave me trouble. The having fun part. I'm afraid I don't know how to do it. Not well anyway. In fact that's one of your greatest charms as far as I'm concerned, your hedonism. Your ability for excess."

"What else?" he said.

"Your intelligence, your sense of humor, your generosity," I said. "Your fairness, the way you are with your kids, your ability to listen and 'be present' except when you're not."

"Nothing bad?" he asked.

I pretended I was thinking about it. "You're a lousy dancer," I said. "And a lousy swimmer."

Mario picked up a long dark cigar to chew on. He frowned. "but you don't dance, and you can't swim," he said.

"True," I said. "But that's why you're perfect for me." I stopped then and leaned back on the couch. "What about the Bocelli concert?"

"Okay," he said. "When he comes to town I'll take you to see him. That is if my legs stop hurting and I'm feeling good enough."

"Promise?" I said. "It really is important to me."

"I promise," he said.

"Pick up your hands so I can be sure you don't have your fingers crossed," I told him, laughing. "I know you."

Holding up his hands so I could see, he said. "If there's any way that I can do it, I will. I promise."

And, so he did.

About the Author

Bestselling author, Carol Gino, RN, MA, was one of the first to reveal the secrets and the shocking truth about what happens behind the closed doors of hospitals, from her first-hand perspective as a nurse for over 30 years. In her blockbuster expose about the healthcare industry (masked as a story), "The Nurses Story" unleashed a Pandora's box and exposed the heart as well as the darkest indignities that Nurses and patients have lived with for centuries.

As a nurse, author, and teacher for over 30 years. She has worked in all areas of Nursing including ER, Intensive Care, Burn Unit, Surgery, Pediatrics, and Hospice Care. Her Masters in Transpersonal Studies focused on new modalities for healing, changes in consciousness, and cross-cultural healing. Carol is the author or co-author of over 8 books, including Los Angeles Times and New York Times bestsellers. She has created several products and online programs for Nurses, Writers and those seeking balance in their lives.

Carol was the longtime companion of the author, Mario Puzo for over 20 years, until his death in 1999, and in 2001 she completed his book "The Family", which was published by Judith Regan of Harper Collins. It was a best seller.

Her latest book, "Me and Mario - Love, Power & Writing with Mario Puzo, author of The Godfather", offers an intimate look into the man, the myth and the magic. A journey of love, friendship, and creative partnership that spanned 2 decades.

*Please Visit
www.meandmario.com
to view the rest of our
Family Album*

You can find Carol at her website: www.carolgino.com
Be sure to sign up to her newsletter to keep in touch!

Facebook: www.facebook.com/meandmario/

Instagram: www.instagram/carolginoauthor/
#carolgino #meandmario

CPSIA information can be obtained
at www.ICGtesting.com
Printed in the USA
BVHW04s1310151018
530224BV00017B/100/P